95p

© 1973 Pye Limited

Produced for Pye Limited by
Daily Mirror Books
IPC Newspapers Ltd.,
79 Camden Road, Camden,
London, NW1 9NT, England.

ISBN 0 85939 016 0

Printed in Great Britain by
Fleetway Printers, Gravesend

ACKNOWLEDGEMENTS

The publishers wish to express their gratitude to the following for their contributions and cooperation in the production of this book:

Associated Television Corporation; EMI/HMV Record Shop, Oxford Street, London; Michael Hodson; Philips Records; Peter Robins; Science Museum, London; Chris Spencer.

PHOTOGRAPHIC CREDITS

Black and white prints: *BBC:* pages 13, 14, 15, 57, 59, 64. *Peter Dunne:* page 67. *Mike Evans/Phonogram:* pages 11, 12. *H. J. Hare & Son Ltd:* page 69 (right). *IPC Electrical-Electronic Press:* pages 86, 87, 94, 95. *H. Jenkins Ltd:* pages 110, 111, 112, 113. *Monitor Press Features Ltd:* pages 16, 99, 100, 101.

Colour transparencies: *BBC:* pages 40, 45, 92, 93. *John Leigh:* page 89. *Chris Spencer:* page 93 (top left).

The photograph of the Thorens phonograph in Britannia Cabinet (page 36) is reproduced by kind permission of its owner, E. Murray-Harvey, Hellesdon-next-Norwich.

the
Pye book
of audio

Pye Limited

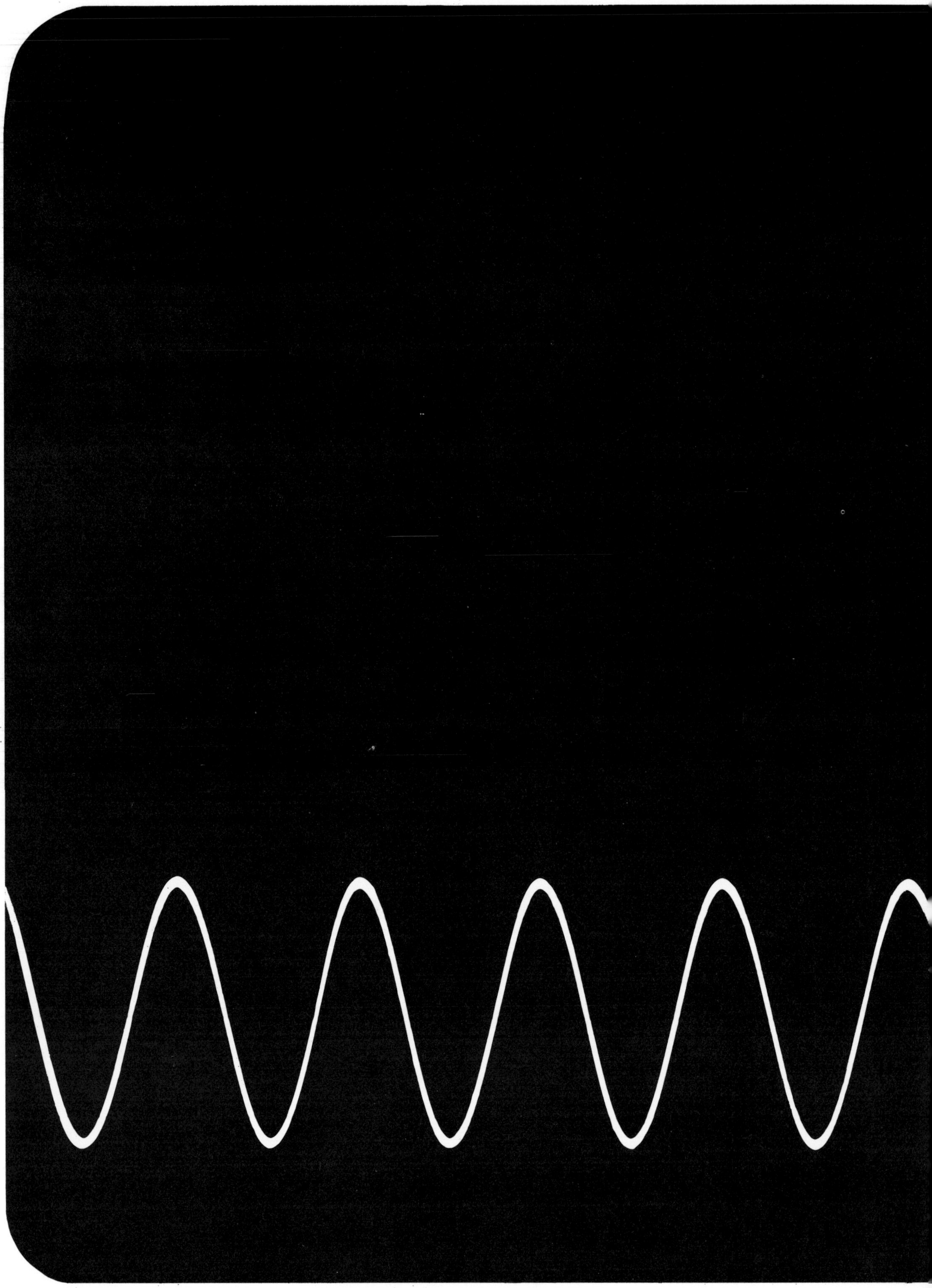

Contents

A foreword by Benny Green

Musician and writer **Benny Green** spent the first twelve years of his professional life playing saxophone in a variety of groups and orchestras ranging from the Stan Kenton band to an Irish country dance group. His jazz reputation was largely founded on his playing with the Ronnie Scott band from 1953-56. During the 1950's he began contributing to musical weeklies, and throughout the decade began to concentrate more and more on writing. He is the regular jazz critic of THE OBSERVER, reviews cinema for PUNCH, and also contributes a weekly column to THE SPECTATOR. His face is familiar on T.V., and his voice on radio, and he has also found time to write three volumes of musical criticism, two novels, the libretto and lyrics of a musical biography of Bernard Shaw, and a one-voice opera in collaboration with John Dankworth (for Cleo Laine at the Bath Festival). He is married and so is his wife. His three small sons, however, are, at the time of going to press, still bachelors.

Some men would be better qualified than others to write an introduction to a book of this kind, but despite my inherently modest nature, I have absolutely no hesitation in claiming that of all those men, none is less suited to the job than I am. I can best define my position by admitting that I dropped out of the technological race on February 11, 1847, on which day, as my more learned readers will know, Thomas Alva Edison, inventor of the Phonograph, was born. I am not joking. When in my fifth year, one of my voluminous collection of uncles and aunts—I forget now which one—showed me how a gramophone worked, I remember gazing at the record whirring round, listening to a few bars of Eddie Cantor singing "Whoopee", and then asking my adult mentor where the man with the voice was hiding. And that, more or less, has been my position ever since, except of course that with stereophonic sound I amended my question to where were the two men hiding, with quadraphonic sound, where were the four men hiding, and so on. Nevertheless, in spite of this blanket ignorance in all things technological, this all-pervading incompetence in things mechanical, this unsullied imbecility in all things electronic, I have no hesitation in endorsing the idea that sophisticated machinery designed for the accurate reproduction of sound is utterly indispensable to the reasonably sane and reasonably intelligent citizen of the modern world, and I propose to devote the rest of this introductory essay to explaining why.

GREAT-AUNT'S STRAWBERRY BLANCMANGE

Back in my infancy, when first I was confronted by that old Brunswick disc of "Whoopee", it did not take me long to see that, with a few refinements, here was a device which could give a great deal of pleasure. I soon found, for instance, that by applying the principles of centrifugal force, a steel gramophone needle placed at the centre of a spinning turntable, could be made to very soon attach itself to dogs, cats, relatives, or any other moving creatures within a radius of fifteen feet. The crunch came one day in the summer of 1934 when a congenitally hysterical great-aunt of mine found three gramophone needles in a portion of strawberry blancmange she was picking at, and had to be transported immediately to Victoria Station, where she was bundled into a first-class compartment of the *Brighton Belle* clutching a third-class ticket and a portion of strawberry blancmange in a chipped dish, and with a note pinned to her bosom addressed to those who were to collect her at the other end to the effect that she was not to be

How an amazing contraption altered the course of my life...

returned to the metropolis until she had stopped gibbering.

As the years of my childhood passed by, so did I, until well before the start of the Second World War I had already begun to anticipate my destiny as a critic by deciding that there were some singers in the world whose performances would be greatly improved by the boring of a fresh hole in their records, a centimetre off-centre from the hole already most thoughtfully provided by the gramophone company. My adult relations, most of whom were utterly unmusical, preferred their records as produced by the factory, and used to forbid me from defacing the family collection in this way. One afternoon in 1938 I was sitting on the floor in my grandmother's kitchen playing some music on an old hand-winder table model, when one of my aunts swept in and gave me a clip round the ear for having bored yet another hole in yet another record. As it happened, this was one record which I had not so much as touched with my faithful screwdriver—my aunt's mistake being explained by the fact that the record in question was by a lady called Kate Smith singing "Love in Bloom". It was this incident which left me, early in life, with that deep and passionate love of justice which inspired me in later years to abstain from voting in General Elections.

I TAKE TO THE SAXOPHONE

But there had to come a time at last when Thomas Alva Edison's amazing contraption altered the course of my life, as it must have altered the course of practically every twentieth century life. In 1942, now a ruthless teenager, I came to the conclusion that as I intended never doing any work, I must become a jazz musician instead, and began to learn how to improvise on the saxophone. And because in time I became able to perform this difficult trick efficiently enough to play in several famous orchestras, to say nothing of one or two musical ones, the question arises, How? The answer is simply: The Gramophone. Only by kind permission of Thomas Alva Edison was it possible for me to study under the powerful microscope of a student's insatiable curiosity the music of the jazz masters, none of whom had been closer to my London home than the beach at Coney Island, many of whom had already been dead for several years by the time I first encountered them. For instance, my deep, and so far abiding affection, for the Iowa cornettist Leon "Bix" Beiderbecke began in 1941, by which time Bix had already been dead for nine years. We all long ago learned to take for granted the presence in our lives of recordings, and are therefore

inclined to forget that this is the first century in the world's history in which it has become possible to become closely acquainted with the statements, either in speech or music, of great minds of past ages. Every jazz musician I ever worked with knows perfectly well that there is a sense in which the most important soloist in the music's history was not Louis Armstrong, or Duke Ellington, or even Charlie Parker, but Thomas Alva Edison, whose machine made it possible for the artistic caprice of the fleeting moment to become a permanent part of posterity's inheritance.

BAKED PUTTY AND BEACH PEBBLES

For me Edison's prototype machine seemed adequate enough, and I was not prepared for the next great step forward which hit me in the early 1950's. To this day I have only the vaguest idea what it was all about, and all I retain of those confusing days are a few terms like Microgroove, High-Fidelity, Diamond Head. The revolution centred around revolutions, just over thirty-three a minute instead of seventy-eight, an innovation to which I responded with bristling indifference. What was so sensational about making the turntable revolve more slowly? I had been doing that before I was ten years old, by weighting down the record with pieces of baked putty, stale bread rolls, and pebbles from Brighton beach. But slowly I realised that there was something different about the quality of the sound produced by this new-fangled adaptation, and in the spring of 1954 I gave in and became the owner of the most complicated piece of machinery I had so far encountered, a contraption whose workings remained an inscrutable mystery but whose function was vital. This was a Pye "Black Box", and I was so sceptical about the whole business, and so convinced that the salesgirl, a pretty little thing with blonde hair and a merry smile on her employer's face, was putting one over on me, that I said to her, "If this is a Black Box, why is the wood brown?"—a question, incidentally, to which nobody has been able to provide a satisfactory answer to this day.

It seemed to me as I staggered home under the weight of my brown Black Box that technology could go no further, but that was twenty years ago and, had I known it, the Audio revolution was only just beginning. A year later I purchased my first tape recorder, and was so innocent of its ways that the first time I got myself in a muddle with the tape, I simply wound it up as though it were a ball of wool. To this day there rests on the shelf of a dusty cupboard in my house what looks like a skein of cinnamon angora wool, but which is actually an illegally taped recording by me of a BBC talk by St. John Ervine on the theme of Bernard Shaw.

I resisted Stereo for a long time, but eventually succumbed. I resisted cassette tape for an even longer time but eventually succumbed. And the only reason I am not clear what it is I am resisting at the moment is that I know that if I make enquiries I will end up with even more machinery. When I bought that Black Box, I felt rather as those nineteenth-century African missionary-explorers must have done when they went looking for the source of the Nile. And when I first brought my tape recorder home, there was a scandalised hush, as though I had somehow managed to introduce an aardvark into the family circle. That was a long time ago, and today the Audio march has reached very nearly every household in Britain. And what is most interesting of all is that the cost of buying speakers and amplifiers and all the rest of the devices available, is falling as sales rise. For considerably less than £100 a man can equip himself today with the machinery for producing music so loud that even Beethoven in his later period would have heard it.

And Beethoven brings me to the most important point of all about the Audio Age, the way it has added a fresh dimension to aesthetic and educational awareness. In the eighteenth century, the man of sensibility returned from the Grand Tour to ruminate on what he had seen, in a library upholstered with books so numerous that with any luck he would need the rest of his life to read them and so avoid doing any work. Today, in addition to a library, modern man can, if he has the sense, collect a library of sound which will extend his grasp of all things to an astonishing degree. Just as I cannot envisage a world without books, so I cannot imagine a world where the masterpieces of Brahms and Duke Ellington, Debussy and Billie Holiday are not there in the room, waiting on the end of a stylus. And although my dependence on those facilities is more or less total, I am well aware that only in the last twenty or thirty years has such an appendage to everyday life been available.

EARS TO HEAR

There, in my anthology of sound, reside Bernard Shaw discussing the lunacy of war, Sir Arthur Sullivan acknowledging the revolutionary potential of the new miraculous Phonograph, Sir John Betjeman reciting his own poems, Groucho Marx singing "Lydia the Tattooed Lady", various actors and actresses performing Shakespeare, Wilde, O'Casey, Shaw and Arthur Miller; various musicians revealing the stupendous architecture of Brahms' Fourth Symphony, Emlyn Williams reading Dickens, Michael Redgrave reading Chekhov, Dylan Thomas. And the hundreds of jazz musicians, from Sidney Bechet to Stan Getz, who have furthered my education and extended my horizons immeasurably. What began as Edison's brainstorm and grew to my teenaged hobby has now become a window on the past as well as a mirror of the future. I may not know the difference between a pickup and a pick-me-up, but I do know that if some of the technological advances of the last thirty years might have been better left undiscovered, at least the Audio revolution has proved to be a benison to everyone with ears to hear. As someone remarked to me on hearing my stereophonic player for the first time, "It brings every member of the orchestra right into your own home". And you know what kind of trouble that can mean.

"The original sound? It can take as many as one hundred separate operations to reproduce!"

Tom Stephenson has that rare combination—the musical feeling and judgement of a professionally-trained singer, plus the experience of a works-trained electrical engineer.

He is the U.K. recording studio manager of Phonogram Ltd., studio administrator of Chappells, and head of the master cutting department of Phonodisc Ltd., which makes records that are heard every day in millions of homes. Once a programme producer with the British Forces Network in Hamburg, he also broadcasts as a singer and studied under Rudolph Bockelmann, the great Wagnerian singer.

While a trainee recording engineer with E.M.I., he helped to record many famous performers and conductors, including Maria Callas, Sir Thomas Beecham, and Sir Malcolm Sargent.

1
The original sound
by Tom Stephenson

The actual manufacture of a record, from the first taping session to the finished disc, is a highly complex, expensive and fascinating process, calling for a wide range of artistic and technical skills. Recording techniques have not only improved immensely over the years but have been tailored to meet the needs of the artistes, the tastes of the record-buying public and the changes in music itself.

There is all the difference in the world between recording classical music and making a 'pop' disc or even middle-of-the-road LP's. It was the growth of the pop groups over the last ten years or so that led to major changes in techniques and in equipment, with recorders growing from 4-track, through 8, to the 16 and even 24-track systems.

To deal first with classical music. The technical demands here are precisely the opposite of pop. The record producers and conductors of a concerto, an opera, or of chamber music, place the microphones as far away from the performers as possible, to get the natural background and resonance of the surroundings, something that is an essential part of any performance. Generally, only 4-track tapes are used. But recently more recordings are being done in eight track for future quadraphonic release. After discussions and rehearsals, a section of the piece is recorded to check balance and over-all sound quality. The artistes listen and discuss with the producer and engineer their feelings and changes they would like. The same section is recorded again and finally that section is approved and the same thing happens throughout the pieces. Once the tapes have been made it is difficult to alter internal balance of instruments, but musical mistakes can be edited out of the tape.

Then again, recording a major work can take weeks or even months. The recording company has to find the right location, very often town halls in Britain or on the Continent; and sometimes temperament—of men as well

In shirt sleeve order, and with microphones strategically sited, the London Philharmonic Orchestra rehearses.

as of prima donnas—creates delays or can mean shifting the recording site from one city, one country, to another, to fit in with artistes' likes and dislikes or other commitments.

But the important point with classical recording is that everyone involved is skilled in both music theory and practice. The pop world is very different.

When, in the late 1950's and early '60's, the groups first emerged, there were many talented young men and women among them, but few, if any, could even read music let alone write it down. Their technique was to use a tape recorder as composers would use music manuscript paper; they "wrote" on the tape and then developed the melody. Very soon it was found that the 4-track recorder was far too limited for this technique and the 8-track system was introduced, to be followed today by the 16-track, especially for the "progressive" pop discs, with their use of unusual, more exciting sounds and complicated devices.

Today, more than half of all recordings made are of originally unscored music . . . and this is how it is done.

Unlike the classical scene, broadly, for pop the smaller the studio the better. One reason is that pop demands very tight rhythm sounds as a basis, and acoustical separation of sounds in the studio is vital. The reverberation time of a pop studio has to be as short as possible, say 0.5 seconds compared with a full second for a large, light music studio. A typical studio will hold up to 40 musicians but you will not see them massed on a stage, as you would at a concert hall, or in an orchestra pit.

The studio is sound-proof, with thick walls, massive double-doors; it has a "dead" sound. The artistes are individually tucked away in "little boxes" which act as acoustic shields; the microphones are placed as close as possible to each artiste so that on the 16-track system each instrument (or group of them) can be recorded on a separate track for maximum separation.

As well as the artistes in the studio at a recording session, there will be a producer from the record company or the group's own producer, and a recording engineer—usually a young man—who has great responsibility and must be a technician, often a diplomat, frequently an interpreter.

A trainee recording engineer needs A-levels not only in mathematics and/or physics, but also in music.

Pop artistes are not always good at explaining exactly what they want. "I want to make it louder" is simple enough, but "I'd like to sound better . . . you know" is another matter.

Temperament is rarer among pop musicians than, say opera stars, but recording sessions can be tense; new artistes in particular become nervous and may cry, "I just can't sing this afternoon". But the producer and engineer have to show endless patience, give confidence and get *something* on the tape. Something can often be enough because, unlike a classical recording, much can be achieved later by the technicians . . . and usually is.

The set-up for a *big* 16-track recording session might be something like this, remembering that each track records only the instruments or artistes noted:

Track 1   Drums
Track 2   Bass guitar
Track 3   Rhythm guitar
Track 4   Lead guitar
Track 5   Piano
Track 6   Organ
Track 7   Trombones (usually 3)

A break in rehearsal provides opportunity for consultation between the principal singers.

Sir John Barbirolli conducting a Henry Wood Promenade Concert at the Royal Albert Hall.

Under the baton of the maestro, the London Symphony Orchestra rehearses for an Andre Previn Music Night.

Track 8 Trumpets (usually 3)
Track 9 Percussion
Track 10 Violins (usually 8)
Track 11 Violas and cello (2 of each)
If there is a choir . . .
Track 12 Girls
Track 13 Boys

That leaves three tracks. Number 14 will be used to record the soloist (or soloists), 15 and 16 are left free for adding in other instruments that may be found necessary at a later date.

The "echo" effect? That is never recorded until the "mixing" stage. The recording engineer literally "mixes" the sounds on the tapes, adding in the artificial electronic echo, if desired, and also perhaps some extra tone colour for certain instruments.

The recording console has 32 microphone input channels and 16 voltage controlled outputs with logic monitoring for all multi-track and quadraphonic recording. The comprehensive correction facilities, enabling the balance engineers to alter drastically the sound picture, have been achieved by using thin film amplifiers smaller than a matchbox.

The console's specifications were first set out by balance engineers and it was then designed and made by specialist electronic engineers using all the very latest developments in the electronics field. It is the most advanced recording console in Europe and because of the development work involved, cost no less than £55,000.

Now you can see why much pop music is said to be "manufactured" rather than composed!

With the immense amount of care that has to be taken in siting instruments and recording a song or performance again and again, line by line if necessary, time and money are involved. An ordinary single by experienced artistes should take one three-hour recording session and a further three hours for mixing. An hour-long LP by an established singer and professional musicians would probably take three, three-hour sessions and six more hours for mixing. But a modern "progressive" pop record can take anything up to 24 hours to record, with a further 12 hours to mix. One notorious recording took the engineer 20 hours a week for 16 weeks.

With the high cost of studio hire and of the 2-inch tape that is used for 16-track recording, plus the cost of musicians, a very ordinary pop record can easily cost £1,000 before the tape has gone to the record-making factory to be turned into a disc!

Transforming the finished tape recording into a disc calls for as many as 100 separate operations. The first step is to copy the signals recorded on the magnetic tape on to some form of disc. The first such disc is known as an acetate, which is an aluminium disc about 14 inches in diameter, covered on both sides with a comparatively soft plastic lacquer. Formerly, the plastic material was mainly cellulose acetate, but today a plasticised form of cellulose nitrate is used.

A V-shaped groove is cut into the lacquer to contain the

Eurovision contest singer and popular recording favourite over the years—Cliff Richard.

musical signal from the tape. This is carried out on a very costly piece of precision equipment, the cutting machine. What happens is that the acetate is clamped and sucked on to a heavy turntable which revolves at the necessary speed—16, 33⅓, 45 and 78 rpm.

Above the turntable is a cutter head which contains, among other things, a sapphire stylus with a V-shaped tip. Around the stylus is wound a small heating coil to warm up the stylus and help it through the plastic material. The stylus is lowered until it just bites into the acetate, forming a groove while slowly moving across the face of the disc by means of a screw feed, giving the familiar spiral groove. Meanwhile, the original tape is being played back and the amplified signal from the tape is fed to the small coils in the cutter head.

As the tape signal current passes through them, these coils develop magnetic fields which act on an iron armature, causing it to vibrate in sympathy. This means that the stylus will oscillate from side-to-side and instead of cutting a straight, or silent, groove it will wander from side to side. On these groove "modulations", as they are called, the long, slow bends represent bass or low-frequency signals, and the short, rapidly alternating bends represent higher-frequency signals. The loudness, or volume, of the signal is provided by the total sideways movement of the stylus; the pitch, or frequency, of the note comes from the number of bends in a given groove length.

The width of a groove may vary from record to record, but an average one would be about 2½ thousandths of an inch, with the depth of the groove just over one thousandth. The spacing between the grooves can often be less than one ten-thousandth of an inch and it is quite common to find 350 grooves side-by-side in the space of one inch of record surface. On one side of a 12-inch record the groove is often more than a quarter of a mile long.

The recording has now been cut on the acetate, but this is far too fragile to work with, so an exact copy is made in metal. The acetate is first cleaned, and then a fine layer of pure silver is deposited upon it, covering every part of the grooves. This makes the acetate electrically conductive. It is mounted on a spindle and suspended in a nickel plating bath. On the bottom of the bath is a slab of nickel, known as the anode, connected to one side of a low-voltage DC supply. The silver layer on the acetate is connected via the spindle to the other side of the DC supply. As the current flows through the bath, the anode slowly dissolves and nickel is deposited on the silver face of the acetate. After about two hours there is a reasonably thick film of nickel on the silver. The newly-formed copy, called the negative, is split away from the original acetate.

On the negative, however, the grooves now stand

Making sure of perfection—singer Matt Munro listens to the playback of a recording.

16

upside down. It is true that this negative could be used to press out a gramophone record but if it was damaged, all the operations, from cutting the acetate onwards, would have to start again. So, a further nickel copy is made as a safeguard. The negative is replaced in the plating bath and more nickel deposited on its face until a new metal copy, known as the positive, is produced, with the groove inward, just as it was on the acetate. This positive may now be played, as an ordinary record, to check sound quality.

Any minute nickel projections in the positive, shown up by clicks in the loudspeaker during the test playing, are now located by microscope and cut away with an engraving chisel, with immense care being taken not to damage the

Former Beatle Paul McCartney during a recording session at the ATV studios.

walls of the grooves.

The positive is plated with nickel once more and now emerges the third and final copy, known as a stamper. This has the grooves upside down, of course. It is trimmed to the correct diameter, a hole is punched in the centre, and it is ready to be mounted on a press to mould the finished record.

A stamper is taken for each side of the record and mounted on a heavy, cored metal block, which can be heated by steam or cooled by water, and which forms one half of the mould assembly. The record labels are placed on the stamper centres, back to front, and a cake of pre-heated record material is placed in the centre of the bottom stamper. The blocks, which have been heated, are closed and pushed between the platens of a 100-ton hydraulic press. While this moulds the record, heating is continued for a few seconds, then cold water is forced through the blocks for cooling. After less than half a minute the ram opens and the completed record is taken off. Waste material is removed with a circular cutter, there is a careful inspection process, and then the record is placed in its liner and later into the appropriate pictorial cover sleeve.

Making a record, as can be seen, calls for the utmost precision. A play-back stylus can audibly detect groove imperfections down to the size of a hundred thousandth part of an inch; the acceleration of a needle tip round the grooves may reach 1,000G; effective needle tip pressure, measured in tons per square inch, can generate sufficient heat to burn up dust particles in the grooves!

What of the future of the record? Recording has reached enormously high standards and the industry aims to maintain them in the latest area of quadraphony. (See chapter **Four Channel Sound**). The boom in Britain of what is called the "in-car-entertainment" market is a pointer— if one were needed—to the fact that despite constant radio music broadcasts, people insist on hearing what they want to hear at the time it suits them, so the life of record or tape in one form or another is assured. It is estimated that no fewer than 500,000 in-car stereo players will have been sold in the United Kingdom during 1973, most of them of the cartridge type.

The U.K. record and tape business was worth £60m. in 1972, at manufacturers' prices an increase of £17m. on 1971. Of that, total tape sales were estimated to be between 12 and 15 per cent.

Undoubtedly, there is a big future too, in the audio-visual field—sight with music. Philips already have a video cassette player which can record from TV and play back, or play from recorded video programmes, and the latest development is a video-disc which plays for 45 minutes and works through the ordinary home TV set. The obvious possibilities are immense.

The main point about it all is that those who provide the wherewithal, be it disc or tape, for us to reproduce either sound or picture are going to great lengths to ensure the quality of the media. So are those producing the equipment on which to reproduce those recordings. ●

"Light years ahead of great-grandfather's wheezing phonograph."

John Borwick, B.Sc., studied in Edinburgh and spent 11 years in the BBC as a studio manager and, later, instructor in programme operations. He is known to a wide circle of professionals and amateur enthusiasts through his many broadcasts and writings. He is Audio Editor of THE GRAMOPHONE and senior lecturer (recording techniques) in the Department of Music at the University of Surrey.

The history of sound recording and reproduction has been one of spectacular progress in the degree of faithfulness with which the reproduced sounds can recreate for the listener all the sensations of being present at a live performance. As each technical problem has been solved, so the designers have set their sights higher and higher: and the process has been an accelerating one.

It took several decades to bring about any great improvement on Edison's and Berliner's primitive machines of the 1880's and 1890's. In more recent times, technical developments have followed each other at quite staggering speed. Thus the lucky purchaser of a modern high fidelity audio system can enjoy music in his home of a quality that seems whole light years ahead of the wheezing phonographs that so impressed our great-grandfathers.

The sounds of music are stored on a gramophone record or a magnetic tape in the form of a fixed pattern. This pattern is a record, in the strict sense, of the fluctuating loudness, pitch and tonal colours produced by the original performers.

To reproduce a recording, we must set the record or tape in motion at precisely the original speed so that the pattern passes the reproducing point in exact imitation of the time sequence of the original performance.

Gramophone records

In the case of a gramophone record,

2 To reproduce the original sound

by John Borwick

the pattern is inscribed in a V-shaped groove, wound in a spiral towards the centre. We lower a fine tipped stylus (needle) into the groove and, in tracing the groove pattern, the stylus is obliged to vibrate (see Fig. 1). The number of vibrations per second (frequency) and the extent of the movement (amplitude) will depend on the recorded pattern, which in turn corresponds to the pitch and loudness of the music.

In the days of the old acoustic gramophones, these needle vibrations were directly coupled to a diaphragm which would set enough air in vibration to reproduce the musical sounds, though not very faithfully. The amount of energy available was small, of course, and elaborate horns were sometimes used to amplify the sound.

Nowadays we prefer to convert the energy of the stylus vibrations into an alternating electric current which we can easily amplify to any desired volume and send along wires to any remote point. Of course this involves us in two stages of conversion, as is shown in Fig. 2.

The gramophone pickup — the business end containing the stylus is known as the cartridge — first converts the mechanical vibrations of the stylus into an equivalent electric current. This tiny electrical signal is amplified to a value sufficient to drive a loudspeaker. Finally, the loudspeaker converts the electrical energy back into mechanical vibrations which send

sound waves to our ears.

A pickup cartridge is essentially an electrical generator in miniature. Two main principles of generation are used. In crystal or ceramic cartridges, the stylus bears against a thin crystal of material which has the property of generating a positive or negative voltage if it is bent one way or the other (see Fig. 3a). Thus stylus vibrations produce an alternating electrical signal directly. The second family of cartridges, which includes moving coil, moving magnet, moving iron, and induced magnet types, relies on the

electromagnetic principle (see Fig. 3b).

It is a well known fact that any relative movement between a magnet and a piece of wire (preferably wound into a coil) will induce an electrical voltage into the wire. All that is required is to attach a tiny magnet or coil to the stylus in such a way that it passes near a coil or magnet, respectively, and electromagnetic induction will do the rest.

Magnetic tapes

Whereas the recorded pattern in a record groove is clearly visible through

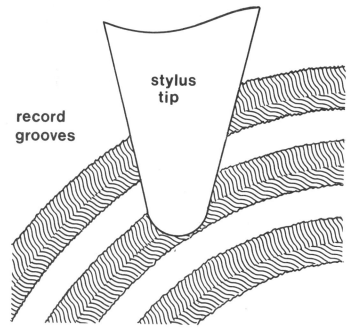

Fig. 1: As groove passes under stylus, the latter traces the recorded pattern and performs equivalent vibrations.

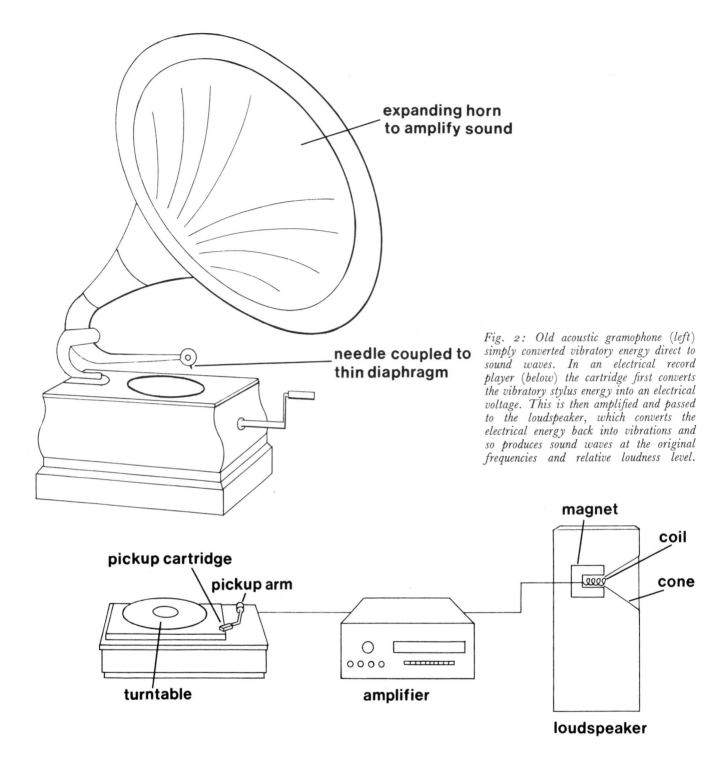

expanding horn to amplify sound

needle coupled to thin diaphragm

Fig. 2: Old acoustic gramophone (left) simply converted vibratory energy direct to sound waves. In an electrical record player (below) the cartridge first converts the vibratory stylus energy into an electrical voltage. This is then amplified and passed to the loudspeaker, which converts the electrical energy back into vibrations and so produces sound waves at the original frequencies and relative loudness level.

pickup cartridge

pickup arm

magnet

coil

cone

turntable

amplifier

loudspeaker

a magnifying glass, a magnetic tape gives no visible clue to the musical signals preserved there. The tape consists of a film backing on which is applied a thin coating or 'varnish' of magnetic material. This is made up of countless miniature magnets of iron oxide (more recently, chromium dioxide has been used). During the recording process, the tape is drawn past an electromagnet (the record head) in which a field, corresponding to the signal current, is concentrated across a frontal gap (see Fig. 4). This tends to orientate the tiny oxide magnets in the tape so that they are formed into a pattern whose density

and frequency of North/South reversal faithfully represents the musical sounds.

On replay, the magnetic pattern on the tape induces a corresponding alternating current in the replay head (another electromagnet — or in the simpler tape machines, a single head may be switched to do double duty as record and replay head). As with gramophone pickups, the electrical signal leaving a tape replay head is much too tiny to drive a loudspeaker directly. So we need to interpose an amplifier.

Amplification of an electrical signal is straightforward enough and could

be accomplished by a simple 'black box' with a volume control on the front. The amplifiers used in hi-fi systems are much more elaborate than this because of the need to provide extra facilities. These include selection of various input signals — pickup, radio tuner, tape machine, microphone — tone controls, filters, stereo balance, tape monitoring etc.

Almost all loudspeakers convert the amplified electrical signal to sound waves by electromagnetic means, as suggested in Fig. 2. A substantial magnet produces a concentrated field in a circular gap in which is suspended a metal coil. When current is passed through the coil, the latter will vibrate and it is affixed to a relatively large cone or diaphragm to give more efficient radiation of sound waves.

Mono or stereo

So far we have concentrated on the processes that enable us to reproduce the sounds of music in terms of the pitch (frequency) and loudness (intensity) of the constituent notes. However, if we are to achieve a feeling of realism in the reproduced sound, we should also give the listener the sensation of hearing the performers spread out naturally across a sort of 'aural stage'. This can never be done with a single reproducing chain and a single loudspeaker.

When we listen to the instruments in an orchestra, or separate out the different voices at a party, we unconsciously analyse the slightly different signals reaching our two ears and, using the experience built up in our early childhood, locate the directions of each sound source quite accurately.

For a sound source to the left of centre, for example, the sound waves reaching our left ear will arrive a little earlier than those reaching our right ear (see Fig. 5); they will also be slightly higher in intensity and will differ in tonal quality due to the obstacle effect of the head.

These clues, tiny though they are, provide the brain with all the localising information it needs and recording techiques, using pairs of microphones, instead of single ones, can capture this information too.

When such two-channel recordings are reproduced through suitably spaced loudspeakers, a realistic spread

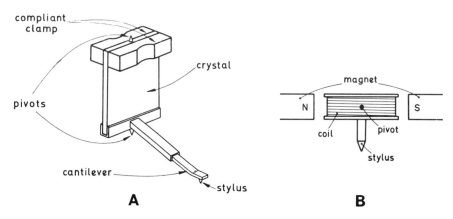

Fig. 3: Comparing the crystal/ceramic (A) and moving coil (B) types of pickup cartridge

of sounds results (see Fig. 6). This is referred to as stereophonic reproduction and a stereo system, though more expensive, is clearly a better proposition than a monophonic (mono) one. Indeed, stereo has so caught on that virtually no mono disc or tape records are made these days.

Nor do we yet seem to have reached

the end of the evolutionary line, so far as man's ingenious efforts to produce absolute realism of sound reproduction are concerned. Just as filling in the arc of sound space between a pair of speakers in stereo adds a whole dimension of pleasure to our musical listening, the researchers are now perfecting techniques to complete

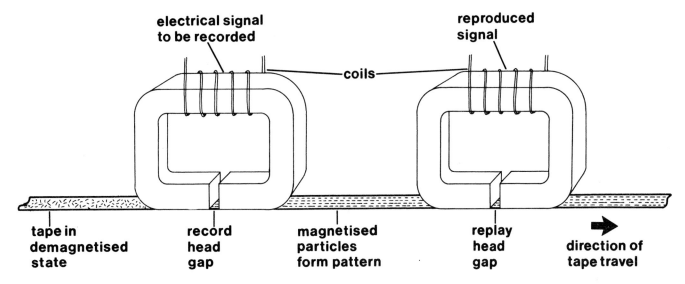

Fig. 4: During recording, the random arrangement of iron oxide particles in the magnetic tape coating is organised into a recorded pattern by the magnetic field across the record head gap. Conversely, on replay, the pattern itself induces a field into the replay head and coil.

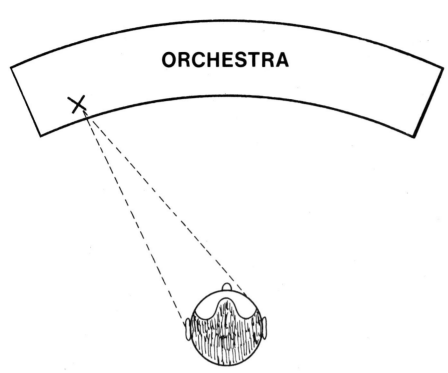

the full 360° circle of sound around us.

Quadraphony is the name given to current methods of using four channels of information, replayed through four loudspeakers around the room. Used properly, this technique not only allows us to pinpoint musical instruments across a wide aural stage, but recreates in our own rooms much of the spacial effect, or ambience, of a real live concert hall, in which a surprisingly high proportion of the total sounds come to us after reflection from the side and back walls.

As the repertoire of quadraphonic gramophone records and tapes builds up, we should see an increasing choice of quadraphonic equipment on which to play them. In the meantime, it is possible to obtain increased ambience from existing stereo records (or broadcasts) by adding the necessary rear speakers and one of the devices available to extract out-of-phase ambient signals. The day of perfect sound reproduction may still be a long way off, but the quest for hi-fi has certainly made long strides in recent years. ●

Fig. 5: Sounds from X will produce slightly different signals at the left and right ears, enabling the listener to identify the direction from which the sounds are coming.

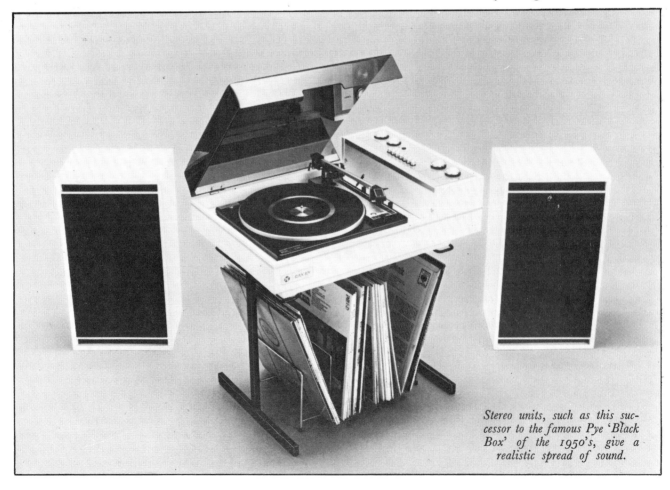

Stereo units, such as this successor to the famous Pye 'Black Box' of the 1950's, give a realistic spread of sound.

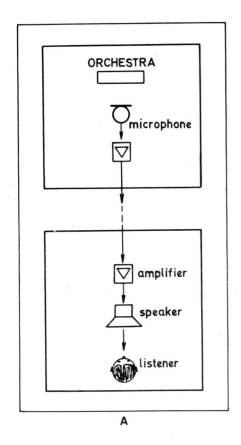

A

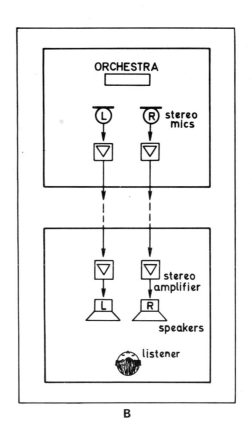

B

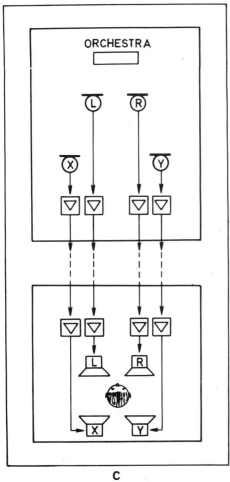

C

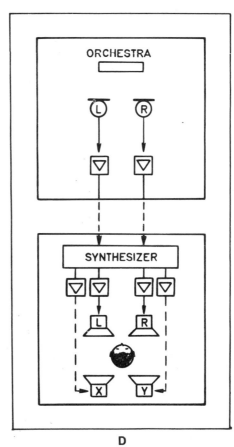

D

Fig. 6: Comparing the record/replay chains for (A) mono, (B) stereo, (C) full quadraphony, and (D) synthesized quadraphony from a stereo signal.

"Stylus tip and record groove: a world of violence and incredible pressures."

Clement Brown has a scientific and musical background. He decided early in his career that the gentle art of communication, rather than an anonymous role in industry, would be most to his taste, and soon he was busy as a publicist and freelance contributor to magazines and newspapers at home and abroad. He has worked as industrial correspondent, compiler of industrial surveys, technical PR specialist, and consultant to firms in the fields of audio and electronics. With 10 books and several smaller publications to his credit, Clement Brown has written on subjects ranging from cars to computers.

Six years ago he started the magazine HI-FI SOUND and remains its Editor. He gives occasional lectures and broadcasts.

In this chapter the aim is to further your understanding of the equipment used to play records. As most experienced record-collectors will acknowledge, some appreciation of ways and means can foster enjoyment of good sound reproduction and ensure that the best possible results are achieved. Besides, a grasp of basics helps the equipment user identify any minor problems and also make simple adjustments that will improve sound quality. As with so many activities, it is better to *know* what is right than to experiment on the basis of inadequate knowledge.

Pickups are made for records. Although we may think of them as products of a complicated modern technology, gramophone records have had a long and distinguished history. Over the years, millions of musically-inclined people have aspired to collections of discs and the equipment on which to play them; and while the interest in recorded music has been sustained we have seen continuous advances in technique — a constant raising of standards in both recording and domestic sound reproduction.

Today, with wide acceptance of hi-fi quality and unit audio of all kinds, the disc record's popularity has reached new heights, and this shows no sign of faltering despite the availability of other sources of music. Record-buying is booming and the vast majority who assemble home music systems — not least the hi-fi enthusiasts — give priority to sound on disc.

First we should look at the record-playing unit and then go on to consider its several parts. In doing so, we should remember that the player in many audio outfits is a separate unit, very much as it is treated in the following explanations. The era of transistors and other miniature devices has, however, made possible the design of some very compact audio, and in certain examples the player is housed together with an amplifier or receiver to form a neat unit which needs only the addition of speakers for stereo reproduction.

To say that a pickup and a turntable are necessary parts of an audio system is hardly a startling revelation. Every-

3
Turning the tables of sound
by Clement Brown

one knows that, of course. The details of these components matter a great deal, though, and the relationship between the two also happens to be important. To begin with, the equipment buyer has a choice between separate components, which he can assemble as a working player if he acquires sufficient expertise, and an integrated, ready-to-use player in which everything is correctly positioned, leaving only the most minor preparations to be made before switching on.

Attention to detail

Integrated players, purchased in chassis form or — more likely — already housed in cabinets, feature in very many audio systems, although some hi-fi enthusiasts choose the more specialised separate parts and undertake the interesting and not unduly difficult assembly job. Whatever the approach, the underlying techniques are similar; and the better the quality of sound to which we aspire, the more careful we must be over details. Attention to detail

at every stage is rewarded in audible terms: carelessness and makeshift will surely lead to disappointment.

The characteristic quality you hear from a hi-fi system is more attributable to the links at the ends of the chain than to those in the middle. The pickup and the loudspeakers make the music. Electronic circuits, the nerve-centre of the system, play their part in guaranteeing accuracy of reproduction and generating enough power for your needs, but the auxiliaries at input and output can more readily impart a distinctive quality to the sound.

How distinctive should this be? Not very: that is the short answer. A 'distinctive' quality may turn out to be a hard, glassy or dim quality, a sound that is obtrusive to a fault or lacking in some obvious way. The best sound reproduction has no unrealistic emphasis or really noticeable features that may become tedious and tiring after a period of listening. Even the inexperienced listener will surely accept the idea that the basic quality is in the programme and that the task of the audio system — as the agency of the programme — is to reveal what is there without imposing new qualities on it.

So it should not be unduly difficult to visualise the role of the pickup. It is the first and most vital link, and it is directly in touch with the stored music in the groove. Much depends on the accuracy with which it traces the

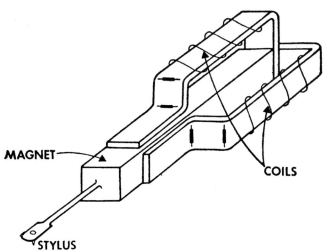

Fig. 1: Principle of moving-magnet cartridge. Stylus is coupled to the magnet, which moves within magnetic circuit. Voltage is set up in the coils.

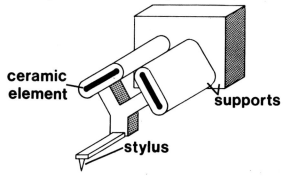

Fig. 2: Principle of ceramic cartridge. Ceramic elements are held in supports and coupled to the stylus. Motion of stylus causes signal voltage to be set up across the elements.

complex information. In the simplest terms its job is to respond to that information and generate a small electrical voltage, an ever-varying flow of impulses representing the programme. This output is the 'signal' — a convenient label used in audio for any information that is being conveyed in electrical form.

A pickup comprises two main items, and it is of interest to consider them apart for in most cases they are designed as separate components. The part containing the stylus and the generator of signals is in the form of a cartridge or head. By convention, a 'head' is a plug-in head intended to fit one specific model of pickup arm.

Very much more common is the 'cartridge', which is the version fitted with a bracket or other arrangement to suit any universal pickup arm, the latter having a headshell and electrical terminations. The user of a universal arm can choose from a variety of cartridges, or exchange one for another during the lifetime of his system, the actual range of choice being determined by the quality of the arm—and *that* is determined by mechanical features to which we return later in this chapter.

We can categorise popular stereo cartridges in a simple way: there are the magnetic cartridges used very widely in unit audio and hi-fi, and there are the ceramic or crystal cartridges found in cheaper instruments such as portable players. There are very obvious differences between these main types. The cartridges employing magnetic principles are generally capable of the best results but cost more than the ceramics. The latter rarely exceed £6 but the magnetic models start at that figure and range up to £40, with a few costing even more.

Another difference shows up in the size of output — the signal voltage generated by the cartridge. Magnetic cartridges generate a much smaller voltage than the other type. It may be only a few thousandths of a volt (for example, five millivolts, abbreviated 5mV) while a quiet passage of music is being reproduced. However, this tiny output is not a disadvantage in practice, as manufacturers encounter no great problem making transistorised amplifiers of sufficient sensitivity to take such a feeble signal for further processing. Hi-fi enthusiasts are perfectly happy

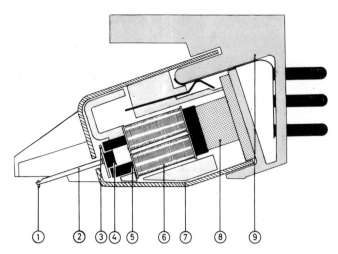

SP15 *cartridge in detail.* 1: *elliptical diamond tip.* 2: *stylus cantilever.* 3: *micro-cross armature.* 4: *suspension.* 5: *polepieces (there are four).* 6: *Coils (four).* 7: *screen round cartridge body.* 8: *magnet.* 9: *bracket with terminals.*

to trade output for quality — and that is exactly what happens where pickups are concerned.

For those who like to know a little more about the underlying principles of these miniaturised and precision-engineered devices, details of operation can be summarised as follows. First the ceramic cartridge: this contains generator elements which, when slightly flexed, produce an electrical voltage. The text-book calls this the 'piezo-electric effect'. Certain ceramic and crystal materials can be used and these, when suitably shaped and coupled to the stylus, are made to respond to the information in the record groove.

Now for the much more important magnetic category. Most readers will have some notion that electricity can be generated by moving a wire near a magnet (movement of the magnet near a fixed wire will do just as well). In fact, like the generators in power stations, all magnetic cartridges work by virtue of the relative motion of magnetic fields and metallic parts. An inventive industry has produced many variations on the theme.

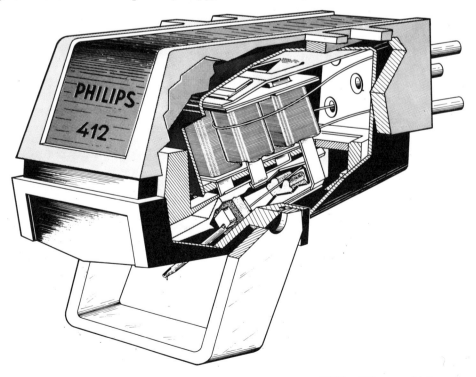

Philips GP412, a high-grade magnetic cartridge.

An especially popular type is the moving-magnet cartridge. In this type the moving part is a tiny pivoted bar carrying at one end the stylus tip and at the other a small magnet—a mere fragment of specially developed material —which vibrates near to the wire coils from which the signal voltages are taken.

In some other examples the magnet and the coils are fixed and the moving part, though not a permanent magnet, is of a magnetic material. Then there is the induced-magnet cartridge in which we find a moving magnetic part and fixed coils, together with a fairly large, fixed magnet, remote from the other parts. Another type, much less common, is the moving-coil cartridge in which the coils are coupled to the stylus and the magnet is fixed.

Whatever the working principle, the aim must be to allow the stylus to move sideways, vertically and in other directions while it is in the record groove; and the designer has to ensure these movements are translated into signals with a high degree of accuracy. Just *why* such uninhibited movements are permitted is not readily put into words: hence the drawing that shows how the stylus is pushed in various directions as it traces the tortuous path of the stereo groove.

The stylus—shaped for sound

Many newcomers to audio are rather confused, at least initially, about the stylus. It was easier to visualise this tiny but vital component's job in the days when it was called a 'needle'. The name described exactly, if not elegantly, the pointed sliver of metal or fibre that traced the waveforms in the record groove, and it was obvious to all that it was part of the fun to take one needle out and put another in. So simple is the basic idea that 'needle' remained in favour when jewel tips had to supersede other materials for playing vulnerable LP discs.

Nowadays the needle is dignified by the name 'stylus'. It is a more scientific name for an even smaller component that has exactly the same function — tracing the stereo groove. Moreover it has to be replaced eventually.

If confusion arises it is probably because the parts incorporating the groove-tracing tip are more critical in design and manufacture and also demand more care in use. Mistakes tend to be expensive. The stylus in fact is quite complex, having several integrated parts which are assembled with great precision, usually inside a plastics moulding. In very many popular magnetic cartridges this stylus-block is pushed into place in the cartridge body and therefore can be removed again when the time comes for replacement.

Typically, the cartridge body contains fixed magnetic parts, including coils, and none of these is likely to wear out. The stylus assembly contains the moving part, which *does* wear out. There are many design variations but the stylus of a moving-magnet cartridge, a much-used type, will serve as an example.

The basis of this stylus is a thin but strong metal tube, pivoted somewhere along its length in a tiny hinge of resilient material (probably synthetic rubber). At one end of this 'cantilever' is fixed the stylus tip, very precisely mounted so that it can enter the groove at the correct attitude. At the other end, beyond the pivot, is a small and light piece of material — a permanent magnet. With the complete stylus in position in the cartridge, the magnet comes close to the magnetic assembly within the body. Motion of the stylus tip in the groove has its counterpart in vibration of the magnet, and so the signal voltage is generated in the coils — a principle that was mentioned earlier.

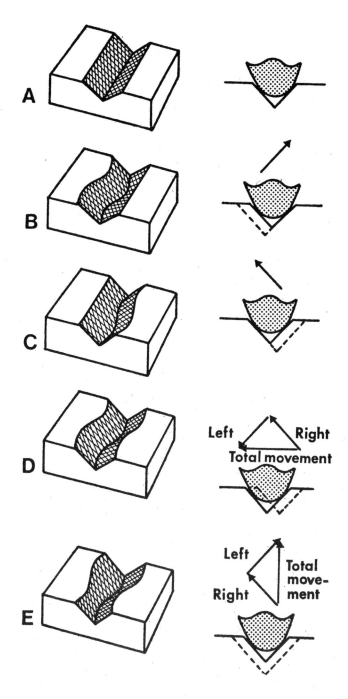

Fig. 3: Stereo disc recording system. A, blank groove, no modulation. B, left channel only is modulated and stylus is moved as shown. C, right channel modulated. D, channels are modulated equally and in phase, so that groove swings from side to side and stylus is moved sideways only. E, channels are modulated equally but in opposition, so that stylus is moved vertically only. In music recording, stylus is moved in these and intermediate directions.

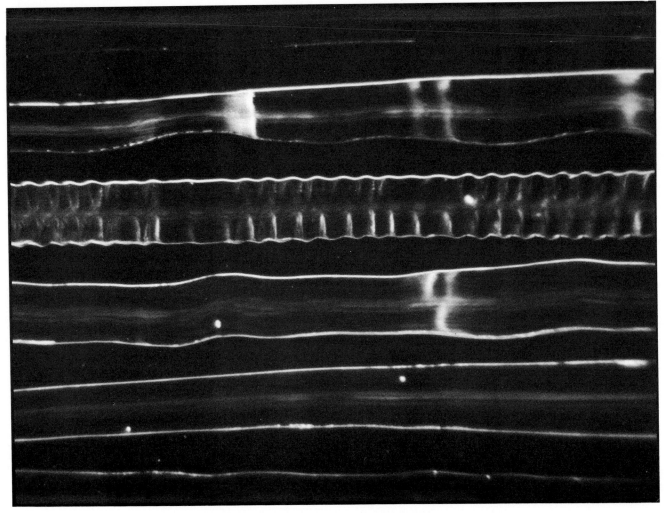

Stereo groove, much magnified. This shows modulations due to voice and guitar.

A stylus in its pivot has a bouncy quality. When it is deflected in any direction the pivot tends to push it back again. Visualise the arrangement: the entire pickup is seen to be resting on the stylus tip when you place it on the record but this also means that the pivot, behaving like a spring, is supporting the entire structure.

This is not unlike the front wheel and suspension of a car. The parts involved there have appreciable weight; they also incorporate a spring, and they support the weight of the car. As the wheel hits a bump the suspension moves and also tends to restore the wheel to its rightful place. The driver, technically minded or otherwise, is grateful for good behaviour of these vital components! The audio equipment user will also benefit from precision in stylus behaviour, for one outstanding requirement is that the tip should maintain contact with the waveforms in the groove.

Many more pages could be filled with a detailed account of stylus design and behaviour, and this would justly

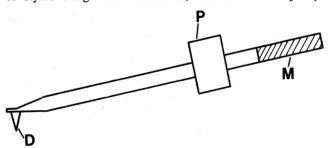

Fig. 4: Stylus assembly of moving-magnet cartridge. D, diamond tip. P, pivot or hinge made of synthetic rubber. M, magnet. The assembly is extremely small and light.

reflect the importance of this diminutive device, especially to the user of hi-fi equipment. But let us single out one topic directly concerned with performance and another that emphasises the link between the music and the listener.

The ever-changing waveforms in the record groove impose enormous forces and accelerations on the stylus, which is deflected with great rapidity in one direction after another. The miniscule world of stylus tip and groove is virtually unseen by the record-user, and certainly it is very much taken for granted, but it is a world of violence and almost incredible local pressures, assessed in many tons per square inch, as well as accelerations that are beyond the reckoning of the most intrepid astronauts.

All this and more is associated with modern pickups that track the record at featherweight pressures yet cause negligible groove-wear. It does, however, mean that the stylus must be extremely light and small. The smaller the load imposed on the groove, the better the result. Consequently the mass pushed about by the groove waveforms may be reduced to a thousandth of a gram (1 milligram) in the best cartridges.

As for the stylus tip: obviously this practically unseen (and all too often ignored) link in the chain must have special qualities to cope with such peculiarly rigorous conditions of use. Great hardness is essential to avoid rapid wear — a worn tip will damage the groove and degrade the sound by chiselling away fragments of the information that has been impressed in the record. All hi-fi styli (and some others) have diamond tips. Sapphire is cheaper but not economic for high quality use because

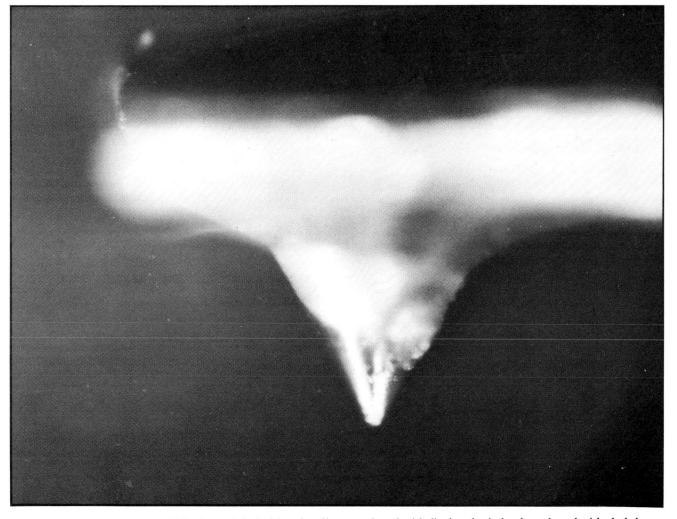

Stylus tip set in cantilever. This diamond tip had been heavily contaminated with dirt but the tip has been cleaned with alcohol.

it wears so quickly. No-one should be surprised at this in view of what has been said about the stresses and strains of record reproduction!

New enthusiasts sometimes wonder whether the stylus diamond is genuine. It is indeed a real diamond — a tiny, shaped fragment, mounted directly into the stylus cantilever in most modern cartridges. In its simplest form it has a conical shape, polished smooth, and the extreme tip that enters the groove is precisely contoured — a hemispherical shape. The radius of its curvature is about a half of one thousandth of an inch.

However, this is not the only tip shape that can be used. Years ago, study of the fit of styli in groove waveforms led to a modified shape, the cross-section at the tip being close to an ellipse. The way this elliptical tip fits into the groove can be judged from the illustration: the widest dimension of the tip is across the groove and the smaller dimension fits more snugly into the waveforms than would be the case with a conical tip.

This elliptical tip happens to be closer in shape to the cutter that forms the groove in the first place — when the original master disc is made prior to record manufacture. It is generally agreed that anything that helps this closer correspondence between recording and replay is likely to be in the interest of accuracy in reproduction.

More important to the listener, though, is the resulting cleaning-up of the sound that is noticed on many records. The elliptical tip, an almost standard item in hi-fi pickups, helps to reduce distortion and promote improved definition of fine detail. An elliptical stylus costs more than a conventional tip, but the reward is audible.

The life of a diamond stylus in a modern pickup depends on conditions of use, notably the presence of dirt in the record grooves. As a rough guide, assuming reasonably clean conditions and intelligent use of equipment, an elliptical diamond in a lightweight pickup of hi-fi calibre is likely to yield about 600-700 hours of use (about 1,800 to 2,100 LP sides) before replacement becomes necessary. Some manufacturers can provide estimates of stylus life based on experience of their own pickups. Obviously it is a good plan to keep a check on playing time, possibly by using a counting device or noting the LPs every week in a notebook kept near the player.

It is also of interest to know that, with most popular ranges of cartridges, replacement of the stylus provides an

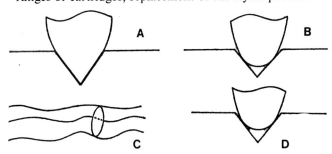

Fig. 5: When the master disc is made, a sharp cutter forms the groove A. B shows a stylus tip in the groove formed by the cutter. This arrangement causes some distortion, but this can be minimised by the use of an elliptical tip. This fits groove modulations more accurately as at C, but its major dimension fits across the groove as at D.

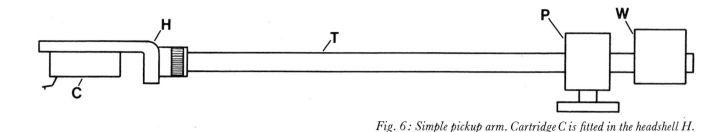

Fig. 6: Simple pickup arm. Cartridge C is fitted in the headshell H. In a hi-fi pickup the arm tube T is set parallel to the record surface. P, pivot housing. W, counterweight to balance arm.

opportunity to change the *type* to be used. The hemispherical tip can be replaced by the elliptical; it is only a matter of pushing in the appropriate stylus assembly. But make sure it is the manufacturer's own branded replacement.

A look at cartridge specifications

The published specification of a cartridge, as found in sales promotion literature or advertising, represents the claims made for the product by its manufacturer. It is a daunting mixture of mechanical and electrical data, but each item reflects some aspect of performance or conceals a warning about conditions of use. Here are a few salient features.

Most people interested in audio soon grasp the idea of frequency range — from 20Hz in the bass, for instance, to 18,000Hz in the extreme treble. A range may indeed be offered, thus: 20-18,000Hz. It is not very informative, though, as it does not indicate any departure from a level response. The statement 20-18,000Hz $\pm$ 2dB (for example) is more useful since it is a true frequency response and tells us that the output may wander 2dB one way or the

other from the desired (though rarely achieved) level condition. A graph showing the response is even better as it shows *where* the deviations occur.

Among the other figures we find one for 'crosstalk' or 'separation' of the stereo channels — a typical quote is 25dB at 1,000Hz. This figure would be somewhat worse—a smaller dB figure — towards the ends of the frequency range. Crosstalk influences the width and general excellence of the stereo image set up by the audio system. Although the average listener would not learn a great deal through concentration on channel separation, it is useful to know that very good figures often go with other good specification data.

Specified 'tracking weight' or 'stylus pressure' is of course the downward pressure of the stylus on the record—one of the most important items. The cartridge manufacturer specifies this, and it is for the user of the complete pickup (cartridge plus arm) to ensure that the pressure is correctly set. If a setting appreciably above the specified top limit is found necessary, then most likely something is wrong with the pickup. A typical range of tracking weight is 1-2 grams.

Among other data will be found the physical weight of the cartridge, probably between 4 and 10 grams. If the pickup arm is designed for modern, light cartridges, then plainly it is silly to mount a very heavy cartridge in it—that would cancel the advantages of the less massive design. Also published are figures on output voltage, distortion and matters affecting the connection of the pickup to the amplifier. It is best to read product test reports in magazines for an interpretation of such facts and figures.

Pickup arms

Now we come to the component that so many people — even hi-fi addicts — find somewhat lacking in interest. Some take it for granted, assuming that such a simple piece of hardware is unlikely to raise any problems; others find it difficult to single out any feature that would lead to a preference for one pickup arm over another. A few enthusiasts cannot quite accept that an uncomplicated arm is good enough for them — surely it should make a more positive contribution to audio quality?

In fact a pickup arm can be both simple and successful, although it must provide a few obvious adjustments — the setting of tracking weight, for instance, and easy fitting of the cartridge. A question can introduce a brief explanation. What is the arm expected to do?

For a start, it is *not* expected to make an audible contribution: that is the last thing we want. But it *is* expected to carry the cartridge in such a way that it can track discs securely at the specified downward pressure. If the cartridge is a delicate modern example intended to track at, say, 1 gram the arm will be a lightweight though precisely made component. Two features are important: the arm will have a small inertia (that goes with the light construction) and the least possible friction in its pivots.

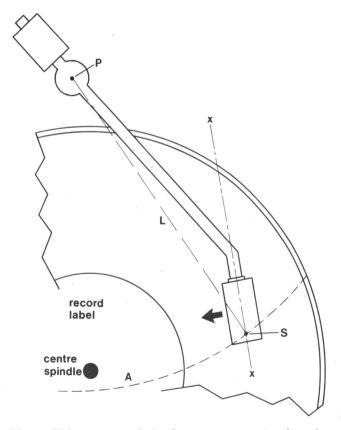

Fig. 7: Pickup geometry. Stylus S moves on an arc A as it tracks the disc. Axis X-X through the cartridge is offset from arm. L is effective length of arm, from pivot P to stylus tip S. Friction of groove past stylus tip causes inward pull (bias) but this can be neutralised by outward correction. Broad arrow indicates bias.

Both attributes enable the pickup to move easily and without restraint in any direction, as is required when the stylus is tracking the slight undulations of a typical LP.

As our illustration shows, the conventional arm comprises a tube with provision for fixing the cartridge at one end. At the other end is a counterweight for balance, and in between are the pivots. It happens to be necessary to ensure the centre-line through the cartridge or head is kept as near as possible a tangent to the groove as the pickup tracks across the disc, and therefore the arm has a bend, called the 'offset', in it.

This way of designing an arm leaves a small and not troublesome error in its tracking pattern. This discrepancy could be eliminated if the arm were straight and arranged to move bodily across the disc instead of pivoting. Indeed, the device used to cut the original master disc is a radial-tracking assembly, and it would seem a good plan to duplicate it when playing the record.

Unfortunately some engineering complications are introduced in such a design, and the resulting component is bound to cost more. An ordinary pivoted arm, with its small geometrical error, is more practicable and a good example is a suitable partner for the most advanced hi-fi cartridges. If this were not so we should all have gone over to straight, radial-motion pickups long ago! As things stand, a pickup arm for hi-fi costs something in the region of £20-35, and there are a few at lower and higher prices.

Correcting 'bias'

A by-product of pivoted-arm design causes some misunderstanding. When a pivoted arm is playing a record, the friction of the groove past the stylus causes the arm to pull inward slightly — toward the record centre. This sidethrust, known to technical folk as 'bias', can be neutralised by a suitable correcting force — a small outward pull. In fact nearly all high quality arms have bias-correction devices such as tiny levers, weights, magnets or springs. This bias effect should not be confused with serious groove-jumping, which is likely to be due to a fault and in any case cannot be corrected by the type of device mentioned here.

Another item that tends to be taken for granted is the turntable. That is not an unreasonable attitude, however,

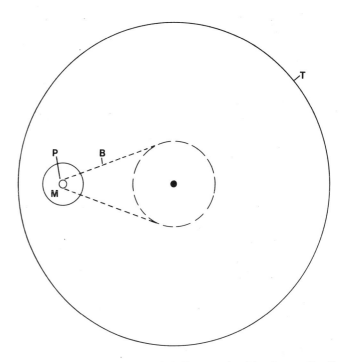

Fig. 9: Belt drive. Rubber belt B transmits drive from pulley P to suitably formed diameter under turntable T. Pulley can have two diameters and the belt can be moved from one to the other to give two-speed operation.

for here our requirement — at its most demanding — is a mechanism that never draws attention to itself. The golden rule is silence. A turntable should rotate reliably, consistently, and above all quietly — and it should go on doing so during the life of the audio system. A really good one, complete with pickup arm, may cost £40 or so; some cost much more.

There is of course a demand for cheaper units, especially for modest stereo outfits, but we cannot expect from them the quiet and unobtrusive running for which the hi-fi enthusiast is prepared to pay a more substantial sum. Least likely to provide a high standard is the cheaper type of automatic instrument known as a record changer; and that is partly because the pickup arm is simply not good enough to provide optimum working conditions for a high-grade cartridge. For those who insist on automatic aids there are some suitably robust and more precisely engineered auto units costing as much as the turntables favoured for hi-fi systems. Automatic pickup set-down and lift-off is a notable feature.

Newcomers viewing the latest products will soon come across the label 'transcription' in connection with turntables. This word, borrowed from professional practice, promises a high standard of rugged reliability: hence its association with hi-fi. Principal attributes are minimal background noise generated in the mechanism (this is known as 'rumble', and enough of it can ruin sound reproduction), the least possible speed fluctuation (this is heard as 'wow and flutter', a disturbance of the pitch

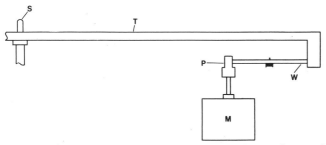

Fig. 8: Two-speed turntable drive. Idler wheel W can be moved against either diameter of pulley P on motor M. Idler drives turntable T.

Zero-100 unit by Garrard has a special pickup arm in which the head is turned during tracking to maintain an attitude tangential to the groove.

and quality of the music), and maximum dependability. The transcription unit leads the field in such respects, but careful selection from cheaper products may sometimes yield results that are nearly as good.

There is much to be said for simplicity in turntables. Until recently the most common type of mechanism involved a rubber-tyred wheel to link the driving motor to the turntable platter, the drive being applied inside the rim. A speed-adjusting control is easily included in this arrangement. A much more familiar system nowadays, especially for units intended for 33 and 45rpm only, employs a rubber belt between a pulley on the motor and a suitable surface beneath the platter. This has been successfully used in designs that tend to minimise 'rumble'.

In the latest generation of turntables we see how electronics can be exploited to provide several novel features. In purely mechanical units, one or more parts must be moved by controls to effect a change of speed (just like changing gear in a car). In electronic units the electrical supply to the driving motor is adjustable and causes the change from, say, 33 to 45rpm. No mechanical parts are affected by this. Further, very small corrections of speed under the user's control are entirely electronically aided; and the in-built circuits can be designed to correct any drift away from the set speed, without any intervention by the user.

A few turntables have a $16\frac{2}{3}$ speed but there have never been any general releases of records at that speed and it

is unlikely that any will appear. Fewer new turntables have the 78rpm speed; but curiously, a number of leading makers of cartridges are offering models with a stylus for 78's. A paradox, many will think!

Summing up

After a guided tour through the complexities of disc reproduction it may be helpful if salient points are brought together and expressed in general terms. The pickup with its stylus takes the key role and precision is the outstanding requirement.

The better the cartridge, the better the sound. But the anticipated results will not be achieved unless the stylus maintains correct contact with the information impressed in the groove. Therefore a high-grade, light tracking cartridge not only deserves but positively demands a pickup arm of suitable quality. Errors here will undermine sound quality and may even prove dangerous for the cartridge.

Background noise can ruin all attempts at hi-fi. Therefore the turntable must contribute the least possible interference, and this becomes steadily more important as audio systems become more ambitious. Constancy of speed is another attribute of a good turntable.

In any audio system the turntable and pickup can be an integrated unit—most are of this kind. Specialised types of arm and turntable are available to meet the demands of enthusiasts who prefer separate components. ●

Modern stereo equipment is neat, attractive and designed to be accommodated in existing room arrangements.

"Interference— too many stations and not enough channels!"

John Charles George Gilbert C.Eng, FIERE, FRTVSoc., FRSA, FBKS is head of the Electronic and Communications Department at the Polytechnic of North London (previously Northern Polytechnic). Other appointments include Technical Editor of MUSIC TRADES REVIEW, 1933, and Technical Consultant to THE GRAMOPHONE. He has also contributed to RADIO ENGINEERING. He is currently Chairman of the Audio Engineering Society, and Vice-President of the Radar & Electronics Association.

In any domestic sound reproducing system the amplifier is the most important single item. Before one can appreciate its functions one must delve a little into the nature of sound. The term "audio" means "I hear" and one must appreciate how and why sounds are produced, how they are picked up, converted into electrical signals, amplified, and then re-converted back into audible sound.

The human ear is able to distinguish between two types of sounds, namely noise and pleasing musical sounds. Musical instruments cause vibrations of a regular nature to be heard by regular variations in the air between the instrument and the listener. Sounds transmitted through air have a speed of approximately 1,087 feet per second when one is at sea level, so if one is sitting in a concert hall some 50 feet from an instrumentalist one hears the sound about a 1/22nd of a second later. In this way one can estimate the distance a storm is away from a listener for the flash of lightning is virtually instantaneous as light travels at 186,000 miles per second, and the associated thunder follows some time later. Roughly each five seconds time interval represents one mile.

In an orchestra, sound vibrations are created either by blowing into an instrument such as a trumpet, scraping a bow across stretched strings as in a violin, or by hitting a stretched diaphragm such as a drum. Music was created long before scientists discovered that the pitch of a musical note was determined by the number of

4
The amplifier and the radio tuner
by John Gilbert

vibrations per second radiated through the air to the ear. In music very few sounds are pure but are a combination of related vibrations of variable complexity, and sounds such as thunder, smashing glass and waves on a seashore being non-repetitive are called noise.

To understand the functioning of an amplifier it is convenient initially to deal with a single pure tone such as that produced by a flute or for scientific purposes by an audio oscillator.

Musical tones

The pianoforte keyboard is a familiar object and usually consists of 88 keys each of which strikes a tuned stretched string. In order that piano music can be played with an orchestra, or can accompany a singer, there must be international agreement as to the pitch of any particular tone. From the scientist's point of view it was agreed that the middle C on the keyboard should vibrate 256 times each second. Below middle C there are normally just over three complete octaves, and above middle C, four octaves. As one moves from one C to the next the number of vibrations is exactly halved when going toward the left hand side of middle C, or doubled as one travels to the right. Thus one can tabulate the piano keyboard in the number of vibrations per second as follows:—

For practical purposes, and by international agreement for the interchangeability of musical instruments having fixed tones such as pianos, organs, the open strings of violins, flutes, etc., a slight modification of the pitch of middle C came into existence. All current instruments are tuned to the A above middle C as 440 vibrations per second which gives middle C the pitch of 261.6 in place of 264 vibrations per second. For scientific purposes earlier textbooks refer to the number of vibrations per second as the number of cycles per second, which is often abbreviated to c/s, but more recently we have come into line with

C^4	C^3	C^2	C^1	C	C^1	C^2	C^3	C^4
16	32	64	128	256	512	1,028	2,056	4,096

Stereo radio tuner and record player combine to produce a versatile sound system.

Echoes from the past

Built around 1900, and based on the Columbia gramophone, this Thorens Swiss-made phonograph used a cabinet known as the Britannia to house the cylinders.

Above: After the first World War there was a rapid development of the technology of tape recording. This (by Boosey and Hawkes) was an early attempt at a portable dictation machine. A clockwork motor drove the tape at $7\frac{1}{2}''$ (190mm) per second and could run for 7 minutes with one winding. The tape was rewound manually.

Left: This unusual type of gramophone, made in 1923, used a pleated diaphragm instead of a soundbox or horn. The needle holder is connected to the centre of the diaphragm. Despite its limited frequency range, the instrument still gives results that are not unpleasing.

Four products from the early days of sound equipment. Top left is an early Berliner hand-driven gramophone built around 1893, and top right, a phonograph manufactured in 1904 by the Edison Bell Company and known as the Edison-Bell Gem. Bottom left is a Columbia gramophone in its most elementary form, marketed at a give-away price to stimulate the sale of cylinders. Bottom right is another early example of a Berliner gramophone made as a toy in 1890.

Above—This early recording machine, known as the Wirek recorder, was manufactured under licence in 1949 by Boosey and Hawkes. It used a technique developed by Camras in the U.S.A., in which a steel wire was magnetised by the amplified microphone currents.

Left—This hand-driven model of 1898 was assembled by the Gramophone Company in London.

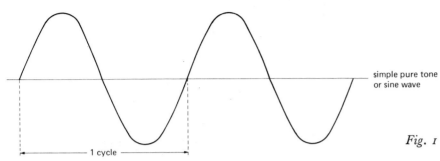

simple pure tone
or sine wave

1 cycle

Fig. 1

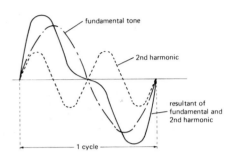

fundamental tone

2nd harmonic

resultant of fundamental and 2nd harmonic

1 cycle

the European term of Hertz, abbreviated to Hz.

Thus the lowest note on an 88-key pianoforte would have a pitch or frequency of 27.50 Hz and the highest note of 4,186 Hz. However, music does not exist of pure tones having only one single frequency, but is of a more complex nature. For example the sound quality of the same pitched note played on a piano is quite different from that played on an oboe, cello or trumpet, and the difference is due to the number of harmonics or overtones added above the fundamental tone. The harmonics have a strict mathematical relationship with the fundamental tone and are exact multiples of that tone. Thus with A=440 Hz, the second harmonic will be 880 Hz, the third=1,760 Hz, the fourth=3,520 Hz, etc. It is the relative sound level of the harmonics and the number of them that give the characteristic sound of a particular instrument.

The human ear, when one is young, is capable of hearing a range of about 10 octaves covering 20–20,000 Hz or 20 Hz–20 KHz. Below 20 Hz the ear does not respond, and it becomes a sensation of feeling and, as no musical instrument produces such a low tone, there is little object in an amplifying system responding below 20 Hz. As one grows older the pitch of the highest note one can hear gradually falls, and at middle age one would not expect to hear frequencies above 15 to 16 KHz. The fundamental pitch of musical instruments does not extend above 5 KHz but the harmonics at 10, 15 and 20 KHz will be audible to a young listener. The sensitivity of the ear varies throughout the musical range and particularly when the sound level is low, thus if music is reproduced at a low level the extreme bass and treble tones become inaudible, but this can be compensated by use of adjustable controls on an amplifier.

If one increases the sound level one

reaches a state of physical pain as exemplified by a nearby jet engine and much research work was conducted by Dr. Harvey Fletcher of the Bell Telephone Laboratories in the USA which resulted in the graphs shown in Fig. 2. The horizontal, or X, axis is marked in Hertz, and can represent the pianoforte keyboard, and the vertical, or Y, axis is calibrated in energy or decibel ratios. The ear, in order to accommodate the enormous energy levels in nature, operates on a logarithmic basis and hence the use of word "decibel", being one-tenth of a Bel, named after the inventor of the telephone, Alexander Graham Bell. The decibel is the smallest increase in sound level that the ear can appreciate in the middle frequency range, and as it only refers to the ratio between two sound levels it is not an absolute standard such as time or temperature. From the graph it will be seen that if one spoke of energy or power ratios one is dealing in astronomical figures but, by using logarithmic ratios, the figures are easier to appreciate.

Intensity level

If one takes two tones and the measured intensity level differs by three decibels (3dB), the louder note will have twice the power and will sound twice as loud, and 6dB difference would be four times as loud, 9dB eight times louder etc. A large orchestra playing in a studio or concert hall with a very low background noise will have a sound intensity of about 90dB.

Now that we have learned a little about sound and hearing, we can use this information in understanding the manufacturer's specification for an amplifier.

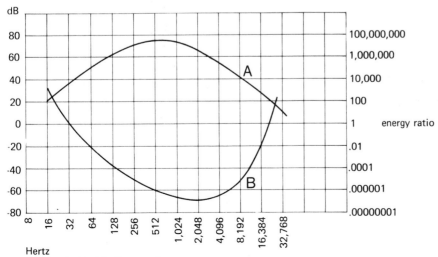

Hertz
A = threshold of feeling or pain
B = threshold of audibility

Fig. 2

Amplification is the key element in any domestic sound system. This stereo unit provides an output of 45 watts RMS on each channel.

The object of an audio amplifier is to amplify the very weak electrical signal derived from a radio tuner, gramophone pickup, tape recorder or microphone to such a level that it will drive a loudspeaker at an acceptable accoustical power level.

In order to achieve this there are several important requirements for a high quality amplifier. (1) It must be capable of handling all audio frequencies without modification of the input signal waveform, and therefore one will require a frequency response from at least 20 Hz to 20 KHz and preferably above the upper limit. (2) It must operate without distorting the signal level or amplitude, that is, it must not overload on very loud passages. (3) The output signal must be an exact magnified image of the input signal introducing the least possible amount of distortion. (4) The amount of background noise and hum should be below audibility otherwise it will be superimposed upon very quiet musical passages.

Fig. 3 shows the basic parts of an amplifier system, a pre-amplifier including correction circuits and tone controls, the power stage, and the power supply which converts the local electricity supply to a form suitable to drive the amplifier. The mains supply

in Britain is standardised at a voltage of 240v although there are still places where the voltage may lie between 200 and 240 volts. The supply is alternating and has the same waveform as a pure musical tone as shown in Fig. 1. The frequency of the alternating current (AC) mains is 50 Hz. In Europe most power supplies operate at either 110 or 220v at 50 Hz, whilst in the USA the voltage is 110–120 AC at 60 Hz.

Sophisticated

Earlier forms of amplifiers were operated by valves which required widely varying voltages to operate the various elements in the valve. For example, the filament that heats the cathode would require 6.3 volts AC whilst the anode voltage would lie between 100–400 volts of direct current

(DC). Such amplifiers required a sophisticated power supply, and the high voltages involved could cause electric shocks. Very few modern amplifying systems now employ thermionic valves and virtually all current equipment makes use of transistors. For the purpose of this book it is not necessary to understand the physics of a transistor, which is a very complex device. Earlier amplifiers used transistors based on germanium and were subject to a short and merry life if operated near their breakdown point. The germanium types have now been replaced by silicon transistors which are capable of operating at higher temperature, and less subject to failure due to overload conditions. Now we will examine the requirements of the various "boxes" that build up an amplifier.

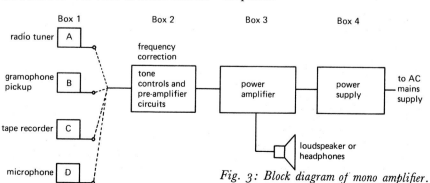

Fig. 3: Block diagram of mono amplifier.

One of the highlights of London's musical year—the series of Promenade Concerts at the Royal Albert Hall. The pictures above and below show Pierre Boulez conducting the B.B.C. Symphony Orchestra during the 1972 Promenade season.

The Shape of Things to Come? This "desk for the man who has everything" incorporates Hi-Fi amplifier, Hi-Fi tuner, stereo tape recorder, cassette recorder, transcription deck and work table for the enthusiast to splice tape and/or film. There is only one snag. When it was designed, early in 1973, Pye Limited had to put a price tag of more than £2,000 on it.

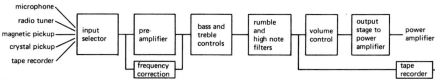

Fig. 4: Block diagram of pre-amplifier.

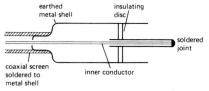

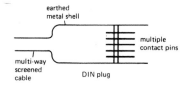

Fig. 5: Coaxial phono socket (far left) and
multi-pin DIN plug (left).

Fig. 3 shows a monophonic amplifier in block form, and as stereophonic amplifiers are merely the addition of a duplicated system which will be considered later, one can analyse the requirements of each section as a mono amplifier chain. The function of each of the input boxes 1a, 1b, 1c and 1d is to provide a suitable signal to Box 2. In this box the circuits ensure that, immaterial of the small signal voltage given from each of the inputs, the signal output is approximately the same level. For example, a modern magnetic gramophone pickup cartridge will produce a signal output of not greater than 10 millivolts, a crystal or ceramic cartridge might give an output of 50–300 mV., a radio tuner up to one volt, and a tape recorder 0.1 to 1 volt. Unless the signal levels were equalised within the pre-amplifier when one switched from one input source to another, there would be a strong possibility of overloading and destroying the power amplifier and damaging the loudspeaker.

The power amplifier, Box 3, will take the output signal from Box 2 and amplify the signal to give a power output commensurate with the requirements for a listening environment, and taking into account the sensitivity of the loudspeaker. Box 4 will provide the necessary voltages and currents required for the pre-amplifier and power stage.

Fig. 4 is a breakdown of the circuits contained in Box 2. On the front panel of the pre-amplifier, which in earlier designs was often a separate unit from the power amplifier, but in most modern designs is integral with the power amplifier and power supply, will be an input selector switch or series of push-buttons. The output signal from the various sources is connected to the pre-amplifier either by co-axial phono sockets (Fig. 5a), or in the case of some Continental designs with multi-pin DIN plugs (Fig. 5b).

The appropriate signal is then fed to a transistor amplifier stage and, in the

case of gramophone records, it is necessary to introduce frequency correction circuits to be the inverse of the disc recording characterisitc. Briefly, in order to have a reasonable playing time on each side of a disc, the recording cutter attenuates, or reduces the amplitude, below about 500 Hz. Also, in order to reduce hiss to acceptable levels, the recording cutter over-amplifies signals above about 1,000 Hz to an internationally agreed characteristic (Fig. 6). In order to reproduce the record without frequency distortion it is therefore necessary to arrange for the lower frequencies to be increased in amplitude, whilst frequencies above 1 KHz are reduced. (Fig. 6.) By adding curve A to curve B the result is a flat frequency characteristic. The microphone, radio tuner or ceramic cartridge will not require any frequency compensation as they should have a flat characteristic. Normally one does not use a microphone with an amplifier combination and more usually it is associated with a tape recorder. However, for public address purposes a microphone is required, and as the signal output is very low, that part of

the amplifier circuit will require the greatest amount of amplification or gain.

Following the pre-amplifier, which may contain several transistors, are the bass and treble controls. Under ideal conditions they should not be required; however, one must compensate for the frequency limitations of loudspeakers and to a lesser extent for the performance of the listening room. Only with the very largest loudspeaker will the reproduced signal extend down to the lowest musical note, and hence with smaller speakers a small increase of bass by means of the tone control will give a more balanced performance. Similarly, as mentioned earlier, as one reduces to volume level the low and high notes disappear before mid-frequency notes, as the ear's sensitivity is greatest in mid-range. Hence a slight increase of the bass and treble controls will restore the audible output to a flatter characteristic.

With broadcast transmissions in the medium waveband the signal is often accompanied with a whistle caused between two stations interfering with

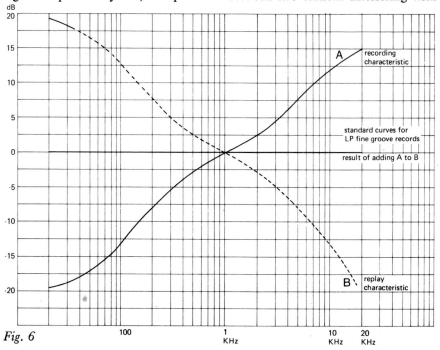

Fig. 6

each other. In this case a slight reduction of the treble control will give a more acceptable result, which might be improved by the use of the sharper high-note cut-off filters. Nearly all amplifier designers make use of an ingenious treble and bass control circuit originally developed by Peter Baxandall and the response curves of such a system are shown in Fig. 7. It will be seen that when the controls are set in the mid-position the response curve is flat, but at 50 Hz one can boost the bass response by about +16dB or cut it by about —17dB. Similarly the treble control at 10 KHz will boost the output by about +17dB or, turning the control anti-clockwise, reduce the treble response by —19dB. Some amplifier designs offer a series of fixed steps for the bass and treble controls but it is more usual to provide variable controls.

Rumble filter

Further amplification follows with several transistors and in the more expensive amplifiers one usually finds additional filters operated by switches. With some record players in the low and medium price range it is possible for the turntable bearings to introduce a very low pitched sound known as

Additional filters, controlled by switches, are usually a feature of high-quality amplifiers.

"rumble", and normally this is lower in pitch than any musical information. To reduce this to more acceptable limits the amplifier will include a rumble filter which will sharply reduce the output below about 30 Hz. This and other fixed filters are normally quoted as so many dB per octave, and this determines the slope of the filter.

Also, in better class amplifiers one finds one or more low-pass filters usually associated with a variable "slope" control. The slope control allows one to vary the angle of cut-off above a certain frequency. Fig. 8 shows typical response curves for low and high pass filters. After the filters will be the volume control which is usually continuously variable. Before this control there is usually an output socket so that one can make a tape recording of any signal sent into the

pre-amplifier and as it is taken before the main volume control, and will usually have an output level of about 100–200 mV., the main volume control will not affect the tape recorder input.

One further control might be found on the front panel, and in particular this applies to amplifiers made overseas. It might be marked "contour", "loudness" or "physio" and its object is to give variable degrees of bass and treble boost as one lowers the volume level. As stated earlier, the ear does not respond equally to all frequencies at all volume levels, and at low levels it is necessary to boost the bass and treble response. Whilst this can be achieved by use of the separate bass and treble controls, the use of a contour control can give a more accurately tailored response at low levels.

As transistor amplifiers generate far

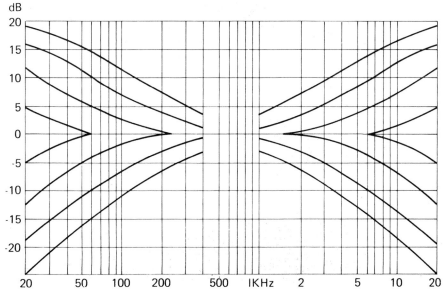

Fig. 7: Frequency response curves for Baxandall-type bass and treble controls.

Production at the Pye Audio factory at Stevenage has expanded by leaps and bounds since it was opened in 1972. The picture below shows workers on one of the production lines at Stevenage, and right, a group at work on the cabinet assembly line.

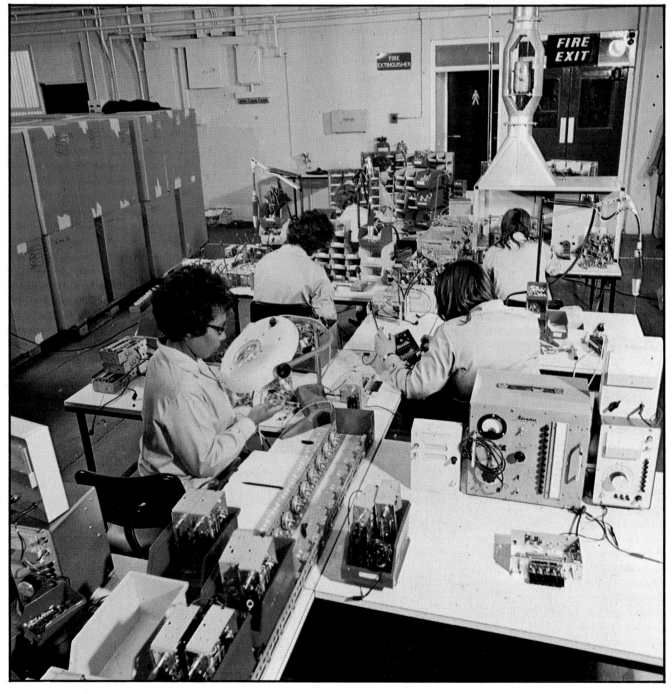

Above: One of radio's most popular disc jockeys, Tony Blackburn, at the control panel during one of his early morning shows for Radio 1.

Nicol Williamson, producer John Tydeman, Rosalind Shanks and Paul Scofield recording a radio version of Othello for the B.B.C.

less heat than valve amplifiers and are less sensitive in picking up unwanted hum noises, it is now common practice to include the power amplifier and power supply on the same chassis as the pre-amplifier. When one reads a manufacturer's specification of an amplifier, the power output is quoted as so many watts. Unfortunately due to a lack of international agreement the same amplifier can be quoted with widely differing wattage figures. It might be quoted in terms of peak power, music power, or RMS watts into a loudspeaker of so many ohms impedance. For example, an amplifier might be quoted as 40 watts peak power, 25 watts music power, or the far more accurate 17 watts RMS and sometimes mention of which power rating has been used is omitted.

So, in choosing an amplifier system we should note how the manufacturer measured the power output and then estimate how many watts will be required for a certain loudspeaker room and its furnishing. This is a difficult thing to estimate because of the number of variables involved. The conversion efficiency from electrical power to acoustical power of the loudspeaker can vary from less than 1% to as high as 35%, but a good average would be 3–5%. In a modest room the average acoustic power required for medium volume level would be in the order of 200–500 milliwatts, and if one assumes that the conversion efficiency of the loudspeaker is 5% then the power amplifier should have a rating of 4–10 watts. However this does not take care of high level peaks that occur in music, called transients, and to allow for these the amplifier rating should be in excess of 15 watts.

The room and its furnishing will have a considerable effect on the loudness for a given power. An empty room with reflective walls and windows will not absorb much of the signal, whilst a room with thick carpeting, heavy settees and armchairs will absorb a considerable amount of

Record player, AM/VHF radio and cassette recorder make up this Dynatron music centre.

the power and particularly at the higher frequencies. In the days of valve amplifiers it was uneconomical to produce power outputs in excess of 10–12 watts, and hence for a given volume level one had to choose a fairly efficient loudspeaker. As you will learn in another part of this book, it is difficult to make a small loudspeaker capable of handling a wide frequency range yet still retaining high efficiency. In the USA a form of loudspeaker was developed that in a fairly small enclosure had a wide frequency response but very low conversion efficiency, probably in the order of 1%.

Fortunately about this time the transistor amplifier had been developed to produce higher output power than valve amplifiers, and figures of 30–100 watts were published. Today, it is possible to purchase amplifiers with a power output of several hundred watts, but these are not necessary for domestic surroundings.

All amplifiers introduce some distortion and it is the skill of the designer to keep the distortion to a minimum. There are two principal forms of distortion that distress the ear, one is harmonic distortion and the second intermodulation distortion. It was stated earlier that musical instruments differ in sound quality by the different harmonics and magnitude of the harmonics that the instrument adds to the pure fundamental tone. But the amplifier should not add or subtract from the information passing through it. Unfortunately, every amplifier adds some harmonic distortion which means that in addition to the basic signal it will add small amounts of second, third, fourth, fifth, etc. harmonics. Second and fourth harmonics represent tones exactly one and two octaves above the input signal frequency, and in small amounts are acceptable. However, the third and fifth harmonics are discordant and cause annoyance. Modern amplifier designs use push-pull output stages

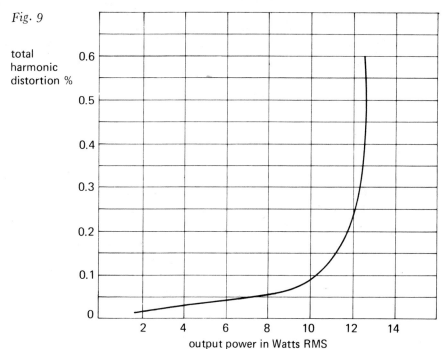

Fig. 9

total harmonic distortion %

output power in Watts RMS

which have the advantage of cancelling out even harmonics, thus reducing the overall distortion.

The second form of distortion is more annoying and is termed intermodulation distortion, and seldom does one find reference to it in manufacturer's specifications except in the highest quality equipment. If one applies two pure tones simultaneously to an amplifier, there is a tendency for one tone to modulate the other. For example, if one has a frequency of

80 Hz and the second 7,000 Hz in an ideal amplifier only those two tones would appear at the output. However, due to the fact that any amplifier introduces distortion however small, one finds at the output additional tones, being the sum and difference frequencies of the input signals. Thus in addition to 80 Hz and 7,000 Hz one would have a trace of 7,080 Hz and 6,920 Hz. Provided these are at a very low level they will be swamped by the basic signals, but if, due to overloading, the intermodulation distortion rises significantly, then the resultant audio signal from the loudspeaker will sound rough and lacking in definition. Fig. 9 indicates the harmonic distortion developed in a good quality amplifier and Fig. 10 shows the form of intermodulation distortion. From Fig. 9 which would be representative of a 12-watt amplifier it will be seen that the total harmonic distortion is less than 0.1% up to 10 watts, and above this it rises steeply and, however much signal is applied to the amplifier, the power output will not exceed 12.5 watts, but with considerable harmonic distortion.

Fig. 8

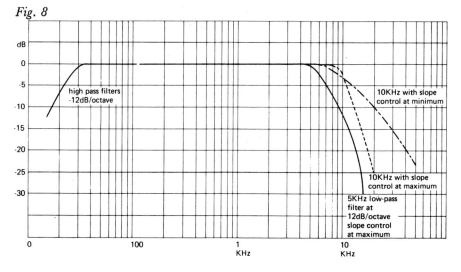

A wide variety of uses has been found in recent years for cassette recorders. Many owners use them for business and family messages to be sent abroad. Others are recording weddings, christenings, birthday parties and other family occasions. The owner of this battery-operated recorder had obviously found his recorder invaluable for putting bird noises on tape.

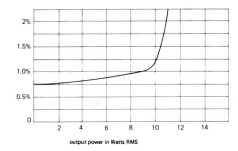

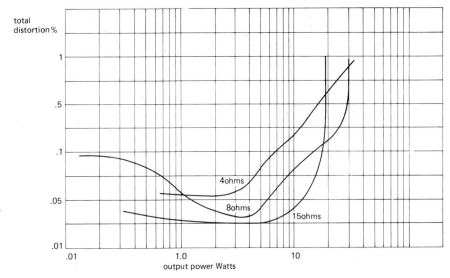

Fig. 10: Power output watts R.M.S. Intermodulation distortion with 80 Hz. and 7,000 Hz. in ratio of 4 to 1.

Fig. 11: The graphs show effect of different impedance loudspeakers plotted against percentage distortion and power output. Amplifier designed for 25 watts into 8-ohm loudspeaker.

Fig. 10 shows the general curve for intermodulation distortion and it is of a similar shape as that for harmonic distortion. Provided that the amplifier is operated at a power output of around 8–10 watts this form of distortion will not be very noticeable but above that it becomes distressing.

One essential condition for the least distortion is the correct matching of the amplifier to the loudspeaker. Older high quality amplifiers, and particularly valve types, were normally designed to have an output impedance of 15 ohms, whilst modern transistor amplifiers are normally designed for 4 or 8 ohm loudspeakers. It is common practice to quote the loudspeaker impedance at 1,000 Hz but at other frequencies it can rise to several times this value. Thus a good loudspeaker may have an impedance of 8 ohms at 1,000 Hz but at its low frequency resonance it might rise to

20–30 ohms. What effect has this on the amplifier? Fig. 11 shows three curves giving the total harmonic distortion plotted against power output for loudspeaker impedances of 4, 8 and 15 ohms, for an amplifier designed to give a power output of 25 watts for use with an 8 ohm loudspeaker.

Knowing the designer's figure for an amplifier's output impedance it is unwise to use a speaker of lower impedance as this can cause damage to the amplifier. The use of a speaker with a higher impedance only has the effect of reducing the power output and will cause no damage.

Stereo amplifiers

Except for portable record players and radio sets, practically all current amplifiers are designed to reproduce stereo gramophone records and stereo broadcasting. Basically a stereo amplifier consists of two identical channels

which should feed a pair of identical loudspeakers. In the broadcasting or recording studio two microphones are used corresponding to the left and right ears. Instruments directly in front of both microphones will produce equal electrical signals in each microphone. Instruments on the left of the orchestra will be picked up by both microphones, but the signal level in the left microphone will be higher as it is nearer, whilst the signal in the right microphone will have travelled a greater distance and arrive very slightly later. Similarly, instruments to the right of the orchestra will produce a higher signal level in the right-hand microphone whilst the left microphone will have a lower signal level slightly later. By combining the two signals they can be broadcast or recorded on disc or tape and then reproduced with a stereo amplifier system. Fig. 12 is a block diagram of a stereo amplifier,

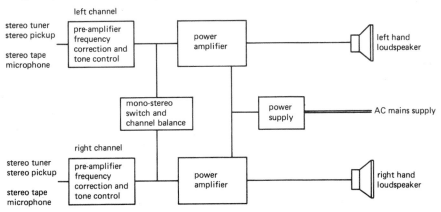

Fig. 12: Block diagram of stereo amplifier.

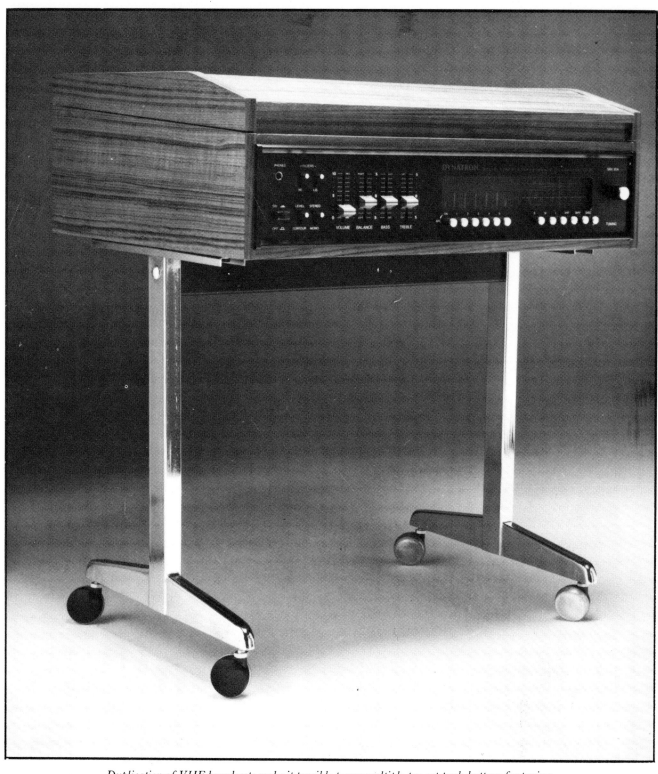

Duplication of VHF broadcasts make it possible to use multiple pre-set push-buttons for tuning.

and its performance requirements are identical to those required for a single channel or monophonic amplifier.

Thus one has two separate pre-amplifier stages, two power amplifier stages, a common power supply and two preferably identical loudspeakers. The additional items are a switch which combines the two loudspeakers in parallel when one is listening to a mono broadcast or tape, and a channel balance control. Under mono conditions the signal will then appear between the two loudspeakers and the image can be moved left or right by means of the channel balance control. Sometimes due to the irregular shape of a listening room or incorrect balancing in the recording or broadcasting studio, or by using a pair of differing loudspeakers, the stereo image can be corrected by use of the balance control.

What, then, are the important points that one should check in a manufacturer's specification? The power output should be quoted in so many watts RMS into 4 or 8 ohms. Watt-age rated in music power is reasonably fair, provided the music does not include long sustained loud passages such as might occur in organ recitals. For high quality equipment the total harmonic distortion should not exceed 0.25% at the rated power. Frequency response should extend from 20–20,000 Hz but it is important that it is quoted between limits and should not be worse than ±2dB. All amplifiers have some background noise and a figure of 50dB or higher is acceptable. Finally, price is a good indication of the value and performance of an amplifier. Often one sees advertisements for amplifiers with an exaggerated, loosely worded specification at bargain prices. Beware! If the better manufacturers could produce an amplifier with a genuine performance at a lower price they would, but research and development is expensive and it must bear a small percentage of the selling price. Keep to the well-established manufacturers and you should enjoy your equipment for many years to come.

Radio tuners

Broadcasting started some fifty years ago and the basic system known as amplitude modulation (AM) is still employed for medium and long wave stations, and for many short wave stations. Such a system has severe limitations in terms of frequency response and dynamic (loudness) range. Everyone has suffered from whistles superimposed on stations and this is due to an interfering station often hundreds of miles away worked on or near the wave-length of the local station. Although there are international agreements fixing the exact wavelength or frequency on which a station should operate, there are far more stations than available channels, and many mid-European stations are outside the agreement.

Stations using the medium and long wavebands can be heard over long distances, but the sound quality is restricted by agreement to not higher than 5.5 KHz which is just beyond the top note of a pianoforte. But all musical instruments generate harmonics which extend to and even beyond the limits of audibility, and hence much of the appreciation of music is limited. For example, a flute produces a fairly pure tone with very little harmonic content whilst a violin is rich in harmonics which gives it its distinctive quality. If both instruments play a 3,000 Hz tone the transmitter cutting off sharply at

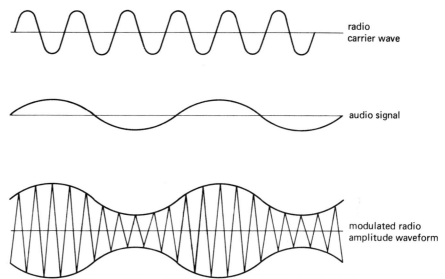

Fig. 13: Transmitted waveform for Amplitude Modulation.

radio carrier wave

audio signal

modulated radio amplitude waveform

5,500 Hz would transmit the flute correctly but would cut off all the violin harmonics, and both instruments should sound the same.

The alternative method of transmission is known as frequency modulation and is a system that can only work in the very high frequency (VHF) or ultra high frequency (UHF) bands. For sound broadcasting purposes the VHF band is used in Europe which extends from 88-108 megahertz (MHz). Such transmissions have a limited range somewhat similar to television transmissions and seldom extend more than 40-50 miles from a powerful transmitter. Hence inter-station interference is eliminated and the audio frequency range can be extended up to at least 15 KHz. Also, as the background noise is less than that associated with AM transmissions, a greater dynamic range is possible.

Fig. 13 indicates the waveforms generated at the transmitter. The carrier wave is allocated a particular wavelength in metres, or frequency in kilohertz. Superimposed on this carrier is the audio signal which causes the amplitude of the carrier to change, and the loudness of the audio signal will determine the peaks and troughs of the resultant combined waveform. In amplitude modulation the system

creates addition frequencies, one either side of the carrier, and the channel width is determined by the highest frequency. For example, if the highest audio frequency is 5.5 KHz then the station will require a channel width of 11 KHz. In the medium waveband covering 200-550 metres (1,500-545 KHz) the total available bandwidth is 955 KHz. If each station requires a channel 11 KHz wide then the total number of stations that can be fitted into the medium waveband is $\frac{955}{11}=86$. But in Europe there are thousands of stations and hence the interference.

Fig. 14 shows the waveform associated with frequency modulation transmissions. In this case the radio carrier wave is of constant amplitude whether an audio signal is superimposed or not. When the audio signal is superimposed the carrier frequency swings about a mean figure and the amount of the swing is called the deviation. In the European VHF system the maximum deviation is $\pm$ 75 KHz which represents the loudest signal level, and very quiet audio signals would only require a deviation of a few kilohertz. Without delving too deeply into the system each station will require a bandwidth of about 240 KHz.

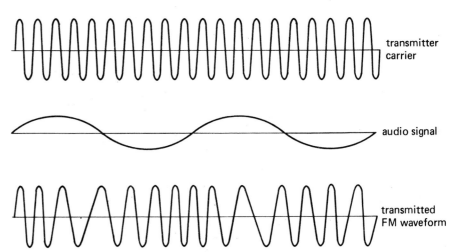

transmitter carrier

audio signal

transmitted FM waveform

FM radio offers many advantages over AM radio the most important being: (1) Elimination of interference between stations due to the limited range of the transmitters and where two stations do operate on the same frequency, the station with the greater signal strength at the receiver will only be heard. This is known as the capture effect and it enables the BBC to operate stations spaced a hundred miles or more apart to transmit on the same frequency, and the receiver will reject the weaker signal. (2) Electrical interference is rejected automatically provided the receiver is well-designed and makes use of an adequate aerial system. (3) Extended audio frequency bandwidth up to at least 15 KHz. (4) The transmitter can be used for stereophonic transmissions which cannot be done with AM.

In the U.K. the available bandwidth in Band 11 extends from 88–100 MHz, which is extended to 104 MHz in Europe and to 108 MHz in the U.S.A. The BBC duplicates the Radio Two, Radio Three and Radio Four programmes on VHF, together with the local broadcast stations. Initially, the Third programme was occasionally transmitted in stereo from the London transmitter at Wrotham but, in recent months, the stereophonic transmissions have been extended to other regions and now also include Radio Two programme material.

Although modern FM tuners are very sensitive and require only an input signal of 1-5 microvolts for full limiting under mono conditions, stereo broadcasting requires a higher signal level. Within the service area of the local transmitter, a simple indoor aerial is often adequate, and usually the manufacturer includes a simple dipole with the tuner. However, to obtain the best performance it is highly desirable to use an external aerial, with a good quality feeder to the receiver. This will ensure a higher input signal and will keep background noise down to the lowest possible level. Also, as the BBC stations are in groups separated by 2.2 MHz, the aerial should have a flat response over some 8 MHz, otherwise the individual stations will give different signal levels at the input to the receiver. Under stereo conditions the transmitter degrades the signal-to-noise ratio by some 20dB and only an adequate aerial system will provide this loss of input signal. As with television one can have ghosting, that is, a signal can arrive at one's receiver over several paths. Although radio signals travel at 186,000 miles per second, there will be a time difference between the direct signal and one bounced off a large building. This will cause distortion and it can be overcome with an aerial system having as much directivity as possible.

The simple dipole has little directivity and although it might pick up an adequate signal level it might also pick up unwanted reflections. In the service area an aerial with one director element will normally be adequate, but near fringe areas a more elaborate aerial will be required probably using a reflector and two director elements. (Fig. 15).

Many modern tuners combine AM medium and long wavebands with FM VHF frequencies. The only advantage in having an AM section is where one is interested in the Radio One programmes which are not radiated on VHF or when one wishes to listen to overseas programmes. If this is not a requirement, then due to the lower quality obtainable on AM, one would never choose to listen to it compared with the high quality VHF transmissions. In the past year or so designers have developed highly stable tuners with multiple pre-set push-buttons and, for most purposes, this form of tuning is ideal, for all the BBC VHF programmes are duplicated throughout the country. However, people living near the Channel coast might prefer to have manual tuning as it is possible to receive nearby Continental stations.

What should one look for in purchasing a tuner or combined tuner-amplifier? If a separate tuner it should include its own power supply, a few

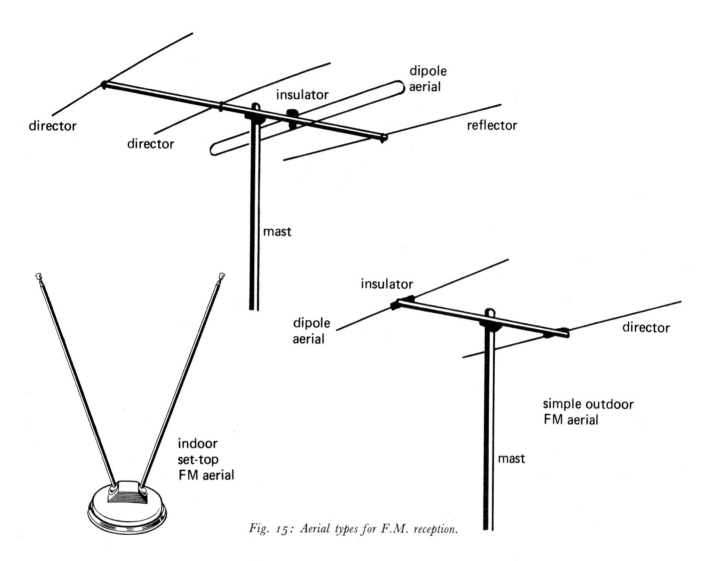

director

director

insulator

dipole
aerial

reflector

mast

indoor
set-top
FM aerial

insulator

dipole
aerial

director

simple outdoor
FM aerial

mast

Fig. 15: Aerial types for F.M. reception.

being designed to take the power from a specific amplifier. The quoted sensitivity for mono reproduction should be between 1-5 microvolts and with a good aerial this will ensure a very quiet background. There should be a tuning meter which when used in conjunction with an automatic frequency control switch will prevent any drifting of the tuner away from the correct tuning point. The output from the tuner should be in the order of 200-500 millivolts (0.2-0.5 volts) and preferably have a pre-set output volume control so that it can be used with any good stereo amplifier. The tuner should include a stereo decoder in order to hear stereo broadcasts. To make a tape recording it should have a multiplex filter which will eliminate unwanted whistles.

Many imported VHF tuners are designed for use with different aerial systems than those commonly used in the U.K. and it might be difficult to purchase a continental type aerial. To overcome this difficulty the tuner should have a coaxial aerial socket which will match British aerial systems.

Normally, AM-FM tuners have an in-built ferrite aerial for medium and long wave reception and seldom does one require an external aerial for these wavebands, but the ferrite aerial will not work on VHF. ●

"One of the most important requirements for reception is a good aerial."

Michael Meyer was born in the Orkney Isles in 1947. After completing his school education locally, he went on to Glasgow and took a BSc (hons) course in Electrical Engineering at Strathclyde University. On graduating in 1969, he joined Mullards as a design engineer at their Central Applications Laboratory in south London, and worked mainly on the circuit design aspects of audio. Early in 1973 he left Mullards to join the BBC's Engineering Information Department as a technical author.

SOUND broadcasting involves the production and transmission of radio programmes. In this chapter we shall describe the latter aspect, together with the problems encountered in receiving the broadcast signal. Particular emphasis will be placed on reception of the high quality "VHF/FM" transmissions.

The audio signal

If we were to plot a graph of the AC mains supply voltage against time, it would look something like the diagram shown in Fig. 1. From this it can be seen that the mains supply alternates from a positive to a negative voltage and back again, and this pattern is repeated indefinitely. In general, this type of continuous to and fro motion is called a "sinewave" oscillation and it has two important characteristics—its amplitude and its frequency. Amplitude is a measure of strength; a weak oscillation (or vibration) has a small amplitude and a strong oscillation a large amplitude (Fig. 2a). The frequency of an oscillation is the number of times it alternates to and fro in the course of one second; a slow oscillation has a low frequency and a fast one a high frequency (Fig. 2b). We used to quote frequency in cycles per second (abbreviated to c/s) but more recently this has been renamed Hertz (Hz) which means exactly the same thing. Thus, nowadays the frequency of our AC mains supply is referred to as "50 Hz". These graphs of amplitude against time, known as waveforms, are very useful when studying the nature of vibrations associated with sounds.

When a tuning fork is struck, the resulting vibration produces variations in air pressure which radiate outwards in the form of sound waves (Fig. 3). Upon reaching our ears, these waves (which travel at about 335 metres per second) are recognised as a fairly pure note of steady pitch. If a microphone is placed in the path of these sound waves, the output cable will carry an electrical signal, generally known as an audio signal, and if the waveform

FIG 1 Graph of AC Mains Voltage against time

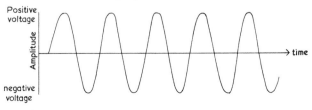

5
The broadcast signal
by Michael Meyer

of this signal is displayed on an oscilloscope (Fig. 4), it will appear as a sinewave oscillation. The frequency of this oscillation will correspond to the pitch of the tuning fork, i.e. a higher-pitched tuning fork will produce an oscillation of higher frequency.

Normally, sound waveforms are not as simple as the solitary sinewave vibration produced by a tuning fork, but contain many vibrations of different frequencies and amplitudes, and these add together to produce a much more complicated waveform. The tonal quality of a musical note depends on the presence of these other vibrations and their relationship to the "fundamental", i.e. the one which determines the pitch. The frequency relationship is often "harmonic", which means they are simple multiples of the fundamental. Since each instrument produces its own characteristic vibrations we can identify the sound associated with an instrument; a piano sounds very different from a guitar or a saxophone. In a similar fashion, the sound waves related to speech also contain many characteristic vibrations and this is how we can differentiate between any two voices. However, it is important to note that the characteristic of a sound also depends a very great deal on its rate of rise and decay.

The sound waves associated with speech, and particularly music, have frequencies in the range from about 16 Hz to upwards of 20,000 Hz, and we usually refer to these as audio frequencies. The range of frequencies that can actually be heard is somewhat less than this; it varies considerably among individuals and the upper limit tends to decrease with age. A figure of about 15,000 Hz is

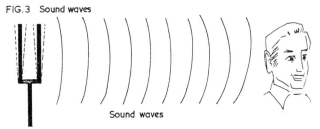

FIG.3 Sound waves

Sound waves

Tuning fork

usually accepted as the upper frequency limit of hearing for the adult ear.

When many instruments are playing, or someone is talking, the complete sound waveform is very complex indeed. The audio signal derived from these sound waves is, likewise, very complicated as can be seen in plate X. This shows the oscilloscope display of an audio signal which was on its way to a Radio 1 transmitter. The horizontal direction represents an interval of time covering about one-thousandth of a second, and the vertical direction the amplitude of the signal measured in volts.

We can convert the electrical energy associated with an audio signal back into sound waves if we amplify the signal and connect it to a loudspeaker (Fig. 5). However, it is also possible to convert electrical energy into another form of energy, electromagnetic waves. More commonly known as radio waves, these travel through space at the speed of light, 300 million metres per second, and can cover much larger distances than sound waves, before they die out. Most radio waves have frequencies much higher than those of sound waves already discussed— the frequencies used for sound broadcasting range from 150,000 Hz up to 100,000,000 Hz. Let us go on to see how we can use these higher frequencies to carry a radio programme (the audio signal) to the sets in our homes.

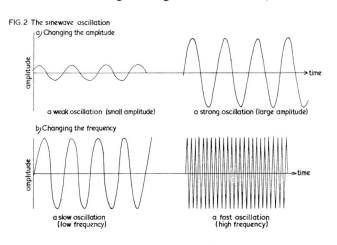

FIG.2 The sinewave oscillation

a) Changing the amplitude

a weak oscillation (small amplitude)   a strong oscillation (large amplitude)

b) Changing the frequency

a slow oscillation (low frequency)   a fast oscillation (high frequency)

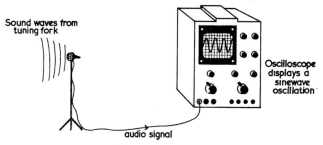

FIG.4 The microphone converts sound waves into an audio signal

Sound waves from tuning fork

Oscilloscope displays a sinewave oscillation

audio signal

Oscilloscope displays: X—audio signal derived from sound; Y(a) and Y(b)—an audio wave and its resulting FM carrier signal.

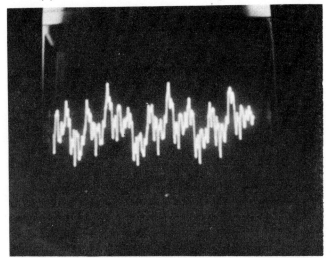

Plate X

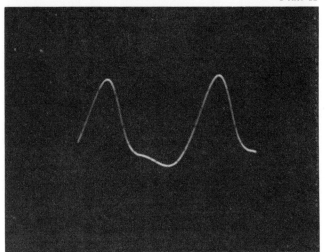

Plate Y(a)

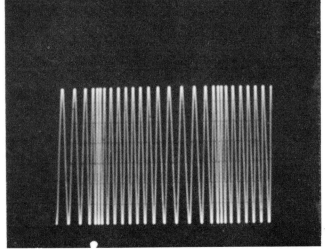

Plate Y(b)

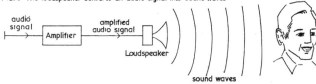

FIG. 5 The loudspeaker converts an audio signal into sound waves

The radio signal

Audio frequencies do not radiate through space as well as higher frequencies do. Thus, in order to convey an audio signal we must first of all generate a powerful oscillation of higher frequency, known as the carrier, and impress the audio signal upon it. The carrier can then be sent to a transmitting aerial and launched into space as a radio wave, carrying with it the audio signal in pick-a-back fashion. These higher frequencies used for the carrier are referred to as radio frequencies (rf), and when quoting them it is often convenient to employ the multiples, kilo,

FIG 6. The units of frequency

Frequency (Hz)	Unit	Abbreviation
I	Hertz	Hz
1,000	Kilohertz	KHz
1,000,000	Megahertz	MHz
1,000,000,000	Gigahertz	GHz

mega and giga, as shown in Fig. 6. Thus, a frequency of one million Hertz can be more simply written as "1 MHz", pronounced "one megahertz". The process of impressing the audio signal on to the carrier oscillation is known as modulation and it can be done in a number of different ways. In sound broadcasting two different methods are employed—amplitude modulation (AM) and frequency modulation (FM).

FIG. 7 Amplitude modulation

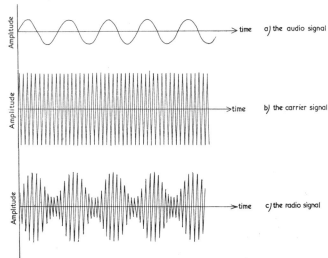

a) the audio signal

b) the carrier signal

c) the radio signal

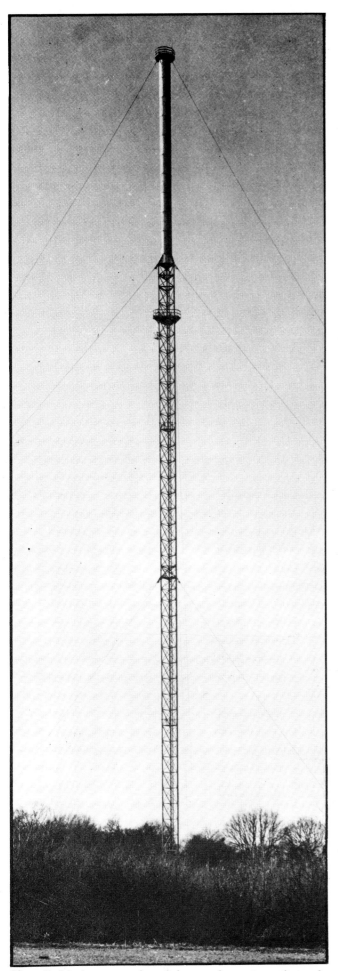

The cylindrical upper portion of the 470 ft. mast constitutes the VHF aerial.

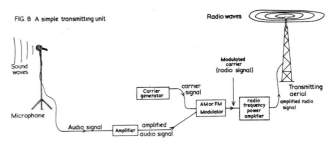

FIG. 8 A simple transmitting unit

Amplitude modulation has been employed since the start of sound broadcasting, which began, in this country, some fifty years ago. The audio signal, represented by a low-frequency sinewave in Fig. 7a, is mixed with the high-frequency carrier oscillation (Fig. 7b) in such a way that the carrier's *amplitude* varies according to the audio signal (Fig. 7c). Frequency modulation, on the other hand, was only introduced in this country during the 1950's. In this case the carrier's *frequency* is made to vary up and down according to the audio signal. Plate Y shows an audio signal and the resulting FM carrier signal, as displayed on an oscilloscope. Either of these modulated carriers, now a complete radio signal, is ready for transmitting. Thus a simple transmitting unit would look something like that outlined in Fig. 8.

Stereo broadcasting

Stereo broadcasting uses a technique whereby *two* separate audio signals (the left and right channels) are radiated by a single transmitter. This is achieved by coding the left and right channels together to form a multiplex signal which is frequency modulated on to a standard carrier. One way to envisage how the system works is to think of it as a process of alternately switching left and right signals on to a single carrier (Fig. 9). A similar switching process at the receiver performs the reverse operation and extracts the left and right signals for feeding to the respective loudspeakers. The switches at the transmitter and in the receiver operate at the rate of 38,000 times per second and are kept in synchronism by a "pilot-tone" signal. The system is fully compatible; that is to say, it allows ordinary receivers to obtain satisfactory mono reception of stereo broadcasts. It is hoped that one day a similar compatible system will be standardized for transmitting four audio signals (quadraphony) so that existing mono and stereo receivers will obtain satisfactory reception of a quadraphonic broadcast.

At this stage in the broadcasting chain, our radio programme has been suitably prepared for transmission as a high frequency radio wave. So, let us now take a closer look at the radio wave itself.

As we saw earlier, a radio frequency signal can be fed to a transmitting aerial and broadcast through space at the speed of light in the form of radio waves. Although these waves travel extremely fast, we do not receive them

Location of long- and medium-wave transmitting stations.

Burghead

Redmoss

Dundee

Shetland
Islands

Orkney
Islands

Westerglen

Glasgow   Edinburgh

Londonderry

Belfast

Lisnagarvey

Dumfries   Stagshaw   BBC Radio Newcastle

Newcastle

BBC Radio Carlisle

Whitehaven   BBC Radio Teesside

Scarborough

Barrow

BBC Radio Leeds   Hull

BBC Radio Blackburn   BBC Radio Humberside

BBC Radio Merseyside   Moorside Edge

BBC Radio Manchester

Penmon   BBC Radio Sheffield

Wrexham   BBC Radio Stoke on Trent

BBC Radio Nottingham   Cromer

BBC Radio Derby   Postwick

BBC Radio Birmingham   BBC Radio Leicester

Tywyn

Droitwich   Daventry

BBC Radio Oxford   BBC Radio London

Swansea   Brookmans Park

Ramsgate

Swindon

BBC Radio Bristol   Clevedon   BBC Radio Medway

Channel Islands

Washford   Folkestone

Barnstaple   Bartley   Fareham   Bexhill

Bournemouth   Brighton

Exeter   BBC Radio Brighton

Redruth   Plymouth   BBC Radio Solent

Start Point

SCALE 20 0 20 40 60 80
miles

EID 167/LP 1:73

58

FIG. 10

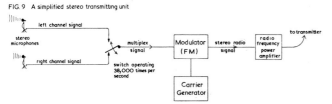
FIG.9   A simplified stereo transmitting unit

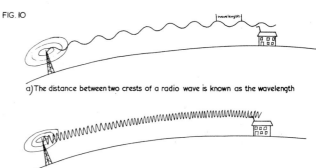

a) The distance between two crests of a radio wave is known as the wavelength

b) Higher frequency waves are more compressed thus the wavelength is shorter

instantaneously. As can be seen in Fig. 10a, when the positive crest of a wave has reached a house the next one is some way behind it. This distance between two crests is the wavelength, and it depends on the frequency of the waves; the higher the frequency the more compressed are the waves and hence the wavelength is smaller (Fig. 10b). To find the wavelength of a radio wave we must divide its speed (300,000 Km per second) by its frequency (in KHz). Thus:

$$\text{Wavelength (in metres)} = \frac{300,000}{\text{Frequency (in KHz)}}$$

or

$$\text{Frequency (in KHz)} = \frac{300,000}{\text{Wavelength (in metres)}}$$

For example, to find the frequency on which Radio 1 transmits we can apply the second of these two formulae, knowing that the wavelength of the station is 247 metres. Thus:

$$\text{Frequency of Radio 1} = \frac{300,000}{247} = 1214 \text{ KHz}$$

Since every transmitter requires a frequency on which to operate, bands of frequencies are allocated to users of transmitting equipment depending upon the purpose of the transmission. Three fre uency bands, also called wavebands, are set aside for domestic sound broadcasting —the long wave, medium wave and VHF bands. The frequencies and wavelengths covered by these three bands along with the various other names given to them are shown in Fig. 11. Note how long-wave stations use frequencies of about 200 KHz and medium-wave stations, 1 MHz. VHF stations use frequencies round about 90 MHz.

The manner in which radio waves travel depends on their frequency and determines the way they can be used.

1. Long and medium waves

During the day, waves of long and medium wavelength travel well along the ground and tend to follow the contours of the earth's surface (Fig. 12). They are, however, weakened as they curve round the horizon and this happens more rapidly with medium waves. Thus, a medium-wave broadcast will not travel as far as a long-wave one of similar power. After dark, medium-wave broadcasts can travel much further because they are reflected from the ionospheric layer in the upper atmosphere (Fig. 13). This results in medium-wave transmitters having different

The Rupert Neve Stereophonic Control Desk in the control cubicle of the BBC Concert Hall at Broadcasting House.

Location of VHF transmitting stations.

Thrumster

Melvaig

Penifiler

Skriaig

Rosemarkie

Grantown ● Meldrum

Kingussie

Fort William ● Kinlochleven

Ballachulish ● Pitlochry

Oban ● Forfar

Perth

Lochgilphead

Toward ● Kirk o' Shotts

Maddybenny More

Campbeltown ● Ashkirk

Ballycastle

Londonderry

Larne

Brougher Mountain ● Divis

Newry

Kilkeel

BBC Radio Carlisle

BBC Radio Newcastle

Pontop Pike ● Weardale

Sandale

Windermere ● Wensleydale ● Whitby

Douglas ● Kendal ● Scarborough

BBC Radio Teesside

Morecambe Bay ● BBC Radio Leeds

BBC Radio Blackburn ● BBC Radio Humberside

BBC Radio Manchester ● Holme Moss

BBC Radio Merseyside ● BBC Radio Sheffield

Llanddona ● Sheffield ● Belmont

Betws-y-Coed

Ffestiniog ● BBC Radio Stoke on Trent

Dolgellau ● Llangollen ● BBC Radio Nottingham

Machynlleth ● BBC Radio Birmingham

Sutton Coldfield ● BBC Radio Leicester

Blaenplwyf ● BBC Radio Derby ● Peterborough ● Tacolneston

Llanidloes ● Northampton

Llandrindod Wells ● Cambridge

Brecon ● Hereford

Haverfordwest ● Churchdown Hill

Carmarthen ● BBC Radio Oxford

Oxford ● BBC Radio Medway

Wenvoe ● Wrotham ● BBC Radio London

Bath

Barnstaple ● BBC Radio Bristol ● Swingate

Les Platons ● BBC Radio Brighton

Okehampton ● Rowridge ● Brighton

North Hessary Tor ● Ventnor

BBC Radio Solent

Redruth

Isles of Scilly

Shetland Islands

Bressay

Orkney Islands

Orkney

● Main station

▲ Relay station

Channel Islands

SCALE 20 0 20 40 60 80
miles

EID 162/LP 1: 73

60

service areas in daytime and night-time. Long waves, to a lesser extent, can also travel greater distances in the evening by "skywave" reflections.

2. VHF waves

VHF waves tend to travel in straight lines and not to follow the curvature of the earth (Fig. 14). They behave rather like light and can therefore be obstructed by hills, large buildings and even trees. VHF waves do not, in general, bounce off the upper atmosphere after dark, which means the service area of a VHF transmitter is usually consistent through day and night.

These different types of "propagation" have a vital effect on broadcasting, because they determine how many stations we can hear and also how well they are received.

FIG. II The three sound Broadcasting Bands

Name of Band	Frequency and wavelength coverage		Other names & Abbreviations
LONG WAVE BAND (low frequency)	150 KHz — 285 KHz	2000 mtrs. — 1053 mtrs.	LW; L; OL; GO,
MEDIUM WAVE BAND (medium frequencies)	525 KHz — 1605 KHz	571 Mtrs — 187 mtrs.	MW; M; AM; PO; OM
VHF BAND	88 MHz — 100 MHz	3-4 m — 3m	FM; U; UK; UKW, Band II

Since long waves travel fairly well over the ground only one high-power transmitter is required to cover virtually the whole country. Medium waves, however, do not travel quite as well over the ground, therefore more stations are required to cover the country. The daytime coverage of long- and medium-wave transmitters is fairly well defined, and several broadcasters throughout Europe can share the same transmission frequency—provided their respective daytime service areas do not overlap. When darkness falls, service areas extend considerably (due to skywave effects) and foreign transmitters sharing our frequencies can severely interfere with domestic services. Hence the distortion and fading on medium-wave stations after dark. Also, it should be noted, sky-

FIG 12 Medium and long waves— day-time

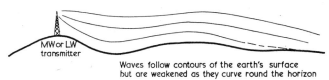

Waves follow contours of the earth's surface but are weakened as they curve round the horizon

waves can interfere with the ground wave from the same station, also causing distortion and fading. This usually occurs on the outskirts of the daytime service area.

Because of the difficulty in providing a good 24-hour service on the long and medium wavebands, broadcasters have recently turned to the VHF band. VHF transmitters have an even smaller service area for a given radiated power, and therefore many more are required to give complete coverage of the country. Since they rely upon "line-of-sight" propagation, many low-power relay stations have to be employed to re-transmit the radio signal into valleys and other areas shielded from the main station. However, VHF transmissions do not suffer from skywave interference after dark, and so the reception quality is consistent through day and night. Furthermore, VHF broadcasts can provide a wide audio bandwith—up to 15 KHz as opposed to the 5.5 KHz audio bandwidth on most long- and medium-wave transmissions. For these reasons, the BBC has built up a network of VHF transmitting stations, bringing its national services on that band to more than 99% of the population. These VHF broad-

FIG. 13 Medium and long waves—night·time

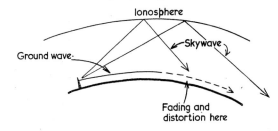

casts overcome the problems of fading, distortion and restricted audio bandwidth associated with long- and medium-wave broadcasts, and by employing the FM system, the signal-to-noise ratio is considerably improved. Another advantage of using FM (instead of AM) is its greater freedom from electrical interference such as that produced by motor ignition systems, refrigerators, etc.

Services available

In the long waveband only one wavelength has been assigned to the United Kingdom—1500 metres. This is used by the BBC for its Radio 2 service transmitted from Droitwich, near Birmingham. In the medium waveband, the United Kingdom has the use of several wavelengths. The BBC's Radios 1, 3 and 4 services are broadcast in this band (from a large number of transmitters throughout

FIG. 14 Vhf waves–day & night

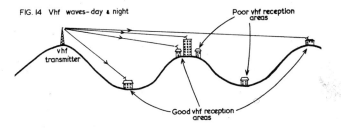

the country), along with Radio 2 in parts of Scotland. Local stations run by the BBC and the IBA also transmit in the medium waveband. All these long- and medium-wave broadcasts use am transmissions.

At each of the VHF transmitting stations in the BBC's network, there are at least three transmitters; two of these are used to broadcast Radios 3 and 4 respectively, whilst the third is shared between the Radios 1 and 2 services. Many of them are already broadcasting in stereophony and the BBC is at the moment extending stereo to the other stations as rapidly as possible. The BBC's and

FIG. 15 A simple radio receiver

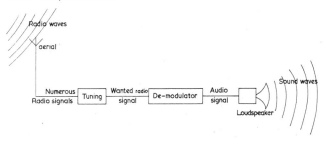

IBA's local stations also broadcast in the VHF band. All these VHF broadcasts use FM transmissions.

Maps showing services available in the United Kingdom are shown with this chapter. Further information on transmitting stations and service areas can be obtained from the BBC's Engineering Information Department and the IBA's Engineering Information Service. Well, let us now turn our attention to receiving the broadcast signals.

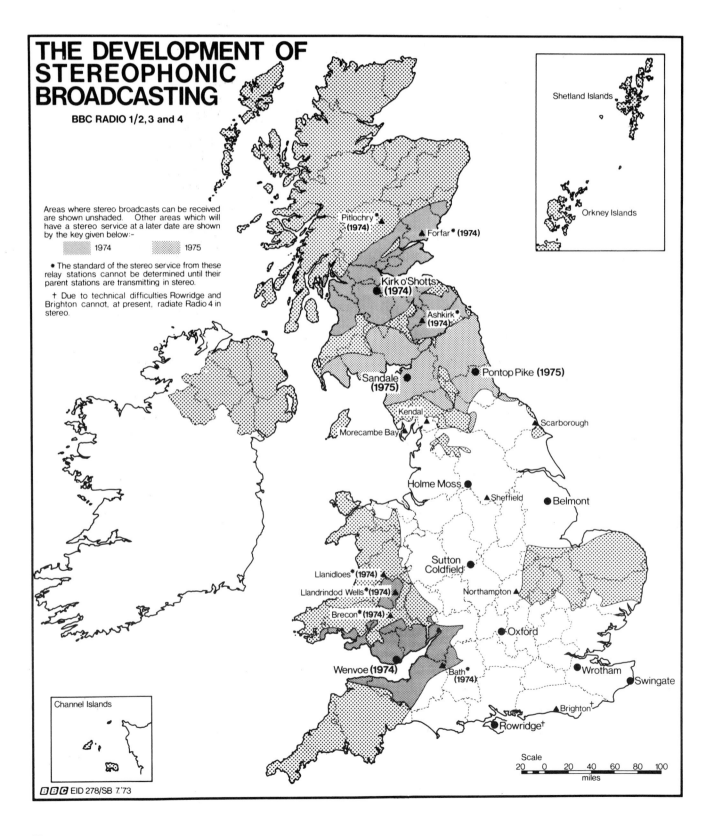

THE DEVELOPMENT OF STEREOPHONIC BROADCASTING

BBC RADIO 1/2, 3 and 4

Areas where stereo broadcasts can be received are shown unshaded. Other areas which will have a stereo service at a later date are shown by the key given below:-

1974   1975

∗ The standard of the stereo service from these relay stations cannot be determined until their parent stations are transmitting in stereo.

† Due to technical difficulties Rowridge and Brighton cannot, at present, radiate Radio 4 in stereo.

Shetland Islands

Orkney Islands

Pitlochry ∗ **(1974)**

Forfar ∗ **(1974)**

Kirk o'Shotts ∗ **(1974)**

Ashkirk ∗ **(1974)**

Pontop Pike **(1975)**

Sandale **(1975)**

Kendal

Scarborough

Morecambe Bay

Holme Moss

Sheffield

Belmont

Sutton Coldfield

Llanidloes∗ **(1974)**

Llandrindod Wells∗ **(1974)**

Northampton

Brecon∗ **(1974)**

Oxford

Wenvoe **(1974)**

Bath∗ **(1974)**

Wrotham

Swingate

Brighton†

Rowridge†

Scale
20 0   20 40 60 80 100
miles

Channel Islands

BBC EID 278/SB 7.'73

Receiving the signal

A receiving aerial is a device which picks up the broadcast signals and feeds them to the receiver. In practice radio waves from many different transmitters will arrive at the aerial, and each one will reproduce its transmitted signal. The first job of the receiver, therefore, is to select the wanted signal from the many that arrive. This is done by "tuning in" to the frequency of the wanted radio signal—signals with a different frequency being rejected. Since a radio signal is too high in frequency to be heard, the next stage is to extract the audio signal from it, a process called demodulation or detection. Finally, the "detected" audio signal must be amplified and converted into sound waves so that the original sounds can be reproduced. These

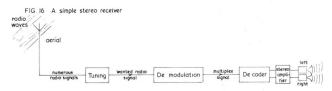

FIG. 16 A simple stereo receiver

simplified processes are outlined in Fig. 15. If the desired transmission is stereophonic, an extra process must be incorporated in the receiver—a stereo decoder will be required to extract the separate left and right channels before connecting them via a stereo amplifier to the two loudspeakers (Fig. 16).

One of the most important requirements for reception is a good aerial. This must be positioned where it can best receive the radio waves of the wanted transmission. Long- and medium-wave sets, often called AM receivers, usually have an internal aerial taking the form of a coil of wire wound on what is called a "ferrite rod". To obtain best reception, the set should be rotated so that the ferrite rod aerial picks up the strongest signal. Sometimes this can also help to reduce interference from foreign stations during the evening.

Some AM receivers have facilities for connecting an external aerial. If such an aerial is required, it can take the form of a length of insulated wire stapled round a picture rail. One end of this wire can be brought down the wall and connected to the set. An outdoor aerial can be made by stringing a length of insulated wire between

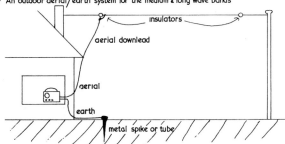

FIG. 17 An outdoor aerial/earth system for the medium & long wave bands

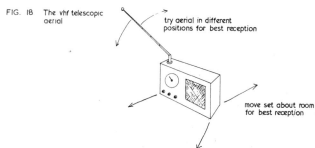

FIG. 18 The vhf telescopic aerial

two high points such as shown in Fig. 17. Both ends of the aerial must be insulated from the supporting structures. An insulated "downlead" then connects the aerial to the set inside the house. If an earthing connection is also required, this can be provided by driving a long metal spike or tube into the ground and taking an insulated lead from this to the earth connection on the receiver (Fig. 17). Alternatively, the receiver earth can be connected by means of a suitable length of wire to a domestic water pipe. On no account should the AC mains supply earth be used as a receiver earth.

VHF portable sets, also known as FM portables, usually

FIG 19 A vhf dipole aerial

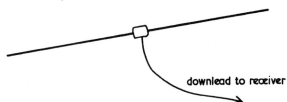

downlead to receiver

have a telescopic aerial, and it may be necessary to experiment with this and the set in different positions in order to get the best possible reception, because the strength of VHF signals can vary considerably over the space of a few feet (Fig. 18). Portable FM sets cannot really do full justice to the high technical quality of VHF/FM transmissions. To make the most of these broadcasts, a high-quality FM tuner coupled to a reproducing system of similar quality will be required, preferably a stereo system. Under these circumstances, it is essential that a proper aerial is provided for the tuner unit: it is senseless to

The pop music studio in the BBC Broadcasting centre at Pebble Hill, Birmingham.

FIG.20 Two element vhf aerial   FIG. 21 Six element vhf aerial

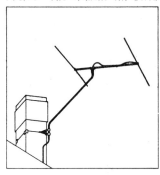
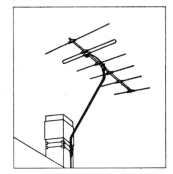

expect satisfactory reproduction of high-quality sound broadcasts if the aerial is not capable of supplying the tuner with a strong input signal.

The prime function of any aerial is to deliver a sufficiently strong signal to the receiver. Apart from the telescopic aerial mentioned earlier, VHF aerials are usually of the "dipole" variety (Fig. 19) and are directional, which means they will respond to signals coming from one or more directions but will discriminate against signals coming from other directions. Further elements (or rods) can be added to a basic dipole to produce an aerial which is both more efficient and more directional. Fig. 20 shows a two-element and Fig. 21, a six-element aerial.

Tall buildings

Since VHF waves can be obstructed by tall buildings, hills, etc. it is essential that the aerial is mounted as high as possible. To pick up the strongest signal, it should be positioned at right angles to the direction of the transmitting station with the rods placed horizontally as shown in Fig. 22. If a multi-element aerial is used, the longest rod should be furthest away from the transmitting station. VHF aerials can also be installed in a loft but the roofing may act as a screen and weaken the signal.

VHF waves can also arrive at the aerial after reflection from a hill or large building (Fig. 23). This may cause unpleasant distortion, and when this occurs a multi-element, directional aerial should be used to discriminate against the unwanted reflected signal. The satisfactory reception of a stereo transmission requires a stronger signal than that needed for receiving a mono broadcast.

FIG. 22 Positioning a vhf dipole

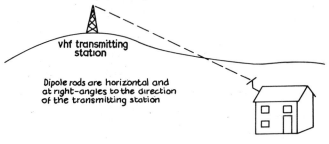

vhf transmitting station

Dipole rods are horizontal and at right-angles to the direction of the transmitting station

FIG. 23 vhf reflections (multipath effects)

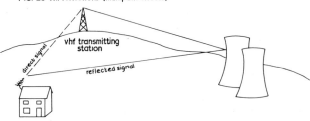

direct signal
vhf transmitting station
reflected signal

Thus, aerials which give adequate mono reception may not necessarily be suitable for good stereo reception. Also, if the signal is weak, reception may be spoilt by motor ignition interference. An efficient multi-element aerial positioned away from traffic routes can usually eliminate this problem—the directional characteristics of this aerial once again discriminate against the unwanted signal.

In general, for mono reception an outdoor dipole should give good results close to the transmitter. Further away from the transmitting station a more efficient (multi-element) aerial will be required. Aerials mounted in a loft may need more elements than an outside aerial would require. And for satisfactory reception of stereo broadcasts extra elements may also be required.

The cost of a proper aerial is small compared with the price of a good tuner, yet the results gained are well worth the expenditure incurred. Further information on reception problems can be obtained from the BBC's Engineering Information Department. ●

"Commercial radio— a new source of audio entertainment, news and information."

Pat Hawker is a principal engineering information officer of the Independent Broadcasting Authority, which he joined in 1968. From 1947 to 1968 he was engaged in technical book and periodical publishing, including several years as Communications Editor of ELECTRONICS WEEKLY. He has written a number of books on radio and television including OUTLINE OF RADIO AND TELEVISION, AMATEUR RADIO TECHNIQUES and GUIDE TO AMATEUR RADIO. Since 1969 he has edited the ROYAL TELEVISION SOCIETY JOURNAL.

A new source of radio entertainment, news and information becomes available to British listeners as a result of the Sound Broadcasting Act 1972—since consolidated into the Independent Broadcasting Authority Act 1973.

This authorised the Independent Broadcasting Authority to set up independent local radio stations throughout the United Kingdom. As for Independent Television, the IBA owns and operates the transmitters; appoints the programme companies; is responsible for programme standards; controls the advertising, and establishes the technical standards.

The first two ILR programme services due to begin in the London area in the autumn of 1973, will be followed by ILR stations in Birmingham, Manchester, and Glasgow in the Spring of 1974. Many other ILR stations will be set up over the following few years, both in major cities and conurbations and also in some smaller cities. Normally, in any given area, there will be only one ILR programme, but an exception is London where there will be two—one a general entertainment service and the other a 'news' station, supplying a news service to other local stations.

The IBA will encourage all the ILR programme companies to run lively, but responsible, local radio services combining popular programming with the fostering of a greater awareness of local affairs and involvement in the community, and with transmissions based on up-to-date engineering techniques and equipment. It is expected, for instance, that on VHF/FM, considerable use will be made of locally-originated stereo, including tapes and discs and stereo-capable distribution link circuits are being provided be-

6 Commercial radio

by Pat Hawker

tween the studio centres and the associated VHF/FM transmitters. Each ILR service will be transmitted over a VHF/FM station in Band II and on an MF (medium-wave) channel.

To encourage the use of high-quality equipment, the IBA, in the Autumn of 1972, published a Code of Practice for ILR studio performance, setting out the operational standards to be aimed at in the studio centres for the tape recorders, disc reproducers, monitoring loudspeakers, acoustics and the like. Stereo transmissions will use the well-established pilot-tone stereo system.

The approximate population coverages of the first five stations—based on VHF/FM service areas—will be London (both news and general stations) 8.5-million; Birmingham 1.7-million; Glasgow 1.9-million; Manchester 2.4-million. In the London area the coverage was planned to include an area bounded roughly by Staines, Harrow, Potters Bar, Epping, Havering, Dartford, Bromley, Caterham, Leatherhead and Chertsey. Similarly the Birmingham VHF coverage will include Bromwich, Burton-on-Trent, Sutton Coldfield, Solihull, Dudley, West Bromwich and Lichfield.

The range of the associated MF transmitters is appreciably more variable and more difficult to define accurately. The maximum range at which good reception will be possible depends upon the season and time of day (since conditions change after dark when MF skywave signals are reflected back to earth from the ionosphere); the level of interference from other stations and from local electrical apparatus; and the efficiency of the receiver and its aerial system. Generally it is hoped to provide a daytime service roughly matching the

VHF service areas—although reception is likely to be possible for some listeners, at some times of the day, at greater ranges.

Among the technical features of the new services will be the general use of circular polarization of the VHF signals and the use of directional aerials at some of the medium-wave transmitting stations.

The use of circular polarization will be significant for motorists and for people listening to VHF/FM stations

John Gorst MP (Left) founder of the Local Radio Association, in Pye's local radio demonstration van.

on portable receivers operated out of doors. At the moment only a tiny minority of British motorists listen to VHF/FM transmission—yet every technically-minded listener recognises the many advantages of VHF/FM over medium waves for good quality broadcasting. The use of circular

polarization provides a more consistent and better signal for listeners using vertical whip-type aerials.

By using directional MF transmitting aerials, it will be possible to operate a number of different ILR services in different parts of the country on the same frequency. For example 261-metres (1151 KHz) will be used in Birmingham, Manchester, Glasgow and in the permanent London station when this comes into operation towards the end of 1974. In London, the ILR services are being launched on MF from a temporary transmitting site in Central London, using temporary frequencies: 417 metres for the LBC news station, 539 metres for Capital Radio.

A great many questions, of course, are still being asked by members of the public. Let me try to answer some of the most common:-

When will independent local radio begin?

In a few areas—London, Manchester, Glasgow and Birmingham—ILR stations will be operating by about the Spring of 1974—in London from about the Autumn of 1973. Early in 1973, experimental test transmissions on MF began in the London area from the temporary station in Chelsea. Many other stations will follow progressively until there are possibly some 60 different ILR services operating throughout the country.

Will ILR stations serve only the very large towns?

No. Some of the services will be set up in relatively small cities.

What about the very small towns and cities?

Coverage of these will depend largely upon how close they are to a main service area; certainly in some areas it will be possible to receive ILR programmes from a nearby large town.

Where will the early transmitters be sited?

London MF transmissions will begin from the temporary station at the Lots Road power station in Central London, using an omni-directional transmitting aerial; the permanent station, which should be operating towards the end of 1974, will be at Saffron Green, near Barnet, and will use directional aerials on 261 metres for the news station and 194 metres for the general station. Both London VHF/FM services will be transmitted from the IBA's television site at Croydon: the news service on 97.3 MHz and the general service on 95.8 MHz.

The Birmingham ILR service will be transmitted on VHF/FM on 94.8 MHz from Lichfield and on MF on 261 metres from Langley Mill.

The Glasgow ILR service will be transmitted on VHF/FM on 95.1 MHz from Black Hill and on MF on 261 metres from Dechmont Hill.

The Manchester ILR service will be transmitted on VHF/FM on 97.0 MHz from Saddleworth and on MF on 261 metres from Ashton Moss.

Which cities and towns will get independent radio after the first seven stations have been opened?

It is expected that at intervals between Autumn 1974 and Summer 1976 stations will start production in the following areas—Bradford, Edinburgh, Ipswich, Liverpool, Nottingham, Plymouth, Portsmouth, Reading, Sheffield, Teesside and Wolverhampton. (This is in alphabetical rather than opening order.)

Thereafter the next nine are likely to be opened at Belfast, Blackburn, Bournemouth, Brighton, Bristol, Cardiff, Coventry, Huddersfield and Leeds. (Also in alphabetical NOT opening order.)

This would give twenty-seven stations with an anticipated population coverage of about 28 million (50%); the eventual target is sixty stations.

These addresses are administrative only and are not the addresses of the studio centres.

Will a new receiver be needed to listen to ILR services?

Most current sets are suitable for the reception of ILR stations. Of course, to obtain the advantages of VHF/FM you need a VHF/FM receiver, and to listen in stereo you need a set fitted with a stereo decoder and twin audio channels. Again, some older medium-wave sets may not cover the whole of the medium-wave band, particularly the sector 1500 to 1605 KHz (200 to 187 metres) where some ILR stations will be operating.

Will ILR stations be on medium waves or VHF?

Normally both simultaneously. It is planned that each ILR area will have both an MF-AM and a VHF/FM transmitter, and it is anticipated that normally both transmitters will open at the same time for a given locality. The long term future of ILR broadcasting is seen resting firmly on the basis of VHF, but the medium-wave back-up is regarded as essential to launch the service as a viable and

ILR Station List

(First seven stations only)

IBA

| Station | MF | | | | | VHF | | | | | | Towns served by VHF Date (MF Comparable) |
	Site	NGR	Frequency (MHz)	Wavelength (M)	Power	VHF Site	NGR	Frequency (MHz)	ERP (kW)	Aerial height (ft.a.o.d.)	Polarisation	
London News	Saffron Green	TQ 216 977	1.151	261		Croydon	TQ 332 696	97.3	2	905	C	1973 Potters Bar, Epping, Grays, Dartford, Caterham, Leatherhead, Staines
London General	Saffron Green	TQ 216 977	1.546	194		Croydon	TQ 332 696	95.8	2	905	C	1973
Birmingham	Langley Mill	SP 160 968	1.151	261		Lichfield	SK 164 043	94.8	2	1400	C	1974 Dudley, Lichfield, Tamworth, Solihull
Manchester	Ashton Moss	SJ 925 994	1.151	261		Saddleworth	SD 987 050	97.0	2	1278	C	1974 Bolton, Bury, Stockport, St. Helens
Glasgow	Dechmont Hill	NS 647 578	1.151	261		Black Hill	NS 828 647	95.1	5	1653	C	1974 Milngavie, Kilsyth, E. Kilbride, Johnstone
Swansea	Jersey Road	SS 681 966	1.169	257		Kilvey Hill	SS 672 940	95.1	1	750	C	1974 Neath, Port Talbot, Llanelli
Tyneside	Greenside	NZ 151 627	1.151	261		Burnhope	NZ 184 474	97.0	5	1407	C	1974 Amble, Durham, Consett

NOTES: 1. Polarisation is either Horizontal (H), Circular (C) or Slant (S). 2. ERP is the maximum effective radiated power. 3. Aerial height is expressed in feet above ordnance datum (ft.a.o.d.).

sound financial prospect in the early years.

Will the medium-wave and VHF/FM stations provide exactly the same service area coverage?

In general terms, the stations are being planned to have roughly comparable coverage on both MF and VHF. But in practice there are bound

Richard Attenborough, chairman of Capital Radio, the company set up to operate one of the first independent entertainment stations.

to be some places where reception will be more satisfactory on one than the other. MF signals are much less affected by local hills and valleys than VHF, but on the other hand MF coverage is greatly affected by the differences in MF propagation during day-time and after dusk. In daytime, MF range depends to a significant extent on the receiver and its aerial. After dusk, the effective range of an MF station tends to be sharply reduced because of interference from distant stations due to the reception of the skywave, and an area of fading due to simultaneous reception of ground-waves and skywaves. The service area of a VHF station remains the same day and night and can generally be more precisely defined.

Will the medium-wave transmitters close down at dusk when the effective coverage shrinks?

No.

Will the technical characteristics of the ILR stations be similar to those of BBC stations?

Certainly there will be no differences that would make receivers which are suitable for BBC stations unsuitable for ILR stations. But one difference is that most ILR VHF/FM stations will transmit circular or slant polarized signals, i.e. signals having simultaneous vertical and horizontal polarization components. This will make it easier for listeners with transistor portable sets and car radios (both of which normally use vertically polarized whip or telescopic aerials) to receive the ILR VHF/FM signals.

Will ILR stations transmit programmes in stereo?

The IBA anticipates that considerable use will be made of locally-originated stereo, including records and tapes, on the VHF/FM transmissions. Stereo capable distribution circuits are being provided between the studios and the local VHF transmitters. The system will be pilot-tone stereo.

Will ILR stations carry programmes only from the local studios?

The IBA are providing distribution circuits which will allow contributions to be transmitted locally from the central news station in London.

Who will build and operate the ILR transmitting stations?

This is the responsibility of the IBA—just as for Independent Television where the ITA (which became the IBA in July, 1972) has always built, owned and operated all transmitters radiating ITV programmes

Will the new ILR stations be co-sited with existing BBC radio stations?

There is no hard and fast rule about this. In a few places, probably yes; in others the ILR transmissions will come from new or existing IBA transmitter sites. Normally the MF station will be at a different site to the VHF/FM transmitter.

Will the fact that ILR and BBC transmissions will often come from different sites have any significance to the listener?

Yes, sometimes. It may mean, for example, that ILR and BBC VHF/FM

stations will be received in some districts at considerably different signal levels, and sometimes from different directions.

Does this mean that for a domestic set, a new VHF/FM aerial may be needed, pointing in another direction?

This may occasionally be advisable, especially for stereo reception where a considerably stronger signal needs to be supplied to the receiver than for monophonic listening, and towards the limits of the service area. On the other hand the directional characteristics of most Band II aerials are fairly broad, without sharp nulls, so that the same aerial will often prove quite adequate. It really all depends on how you are located in respect to the

John Whitney, Managing Director of Capital Radio.

two transmitting stations. In some cases it may be advisable to re-orientate a receiving aerial to obtain a good balance between the various transmissions, or possibly to eliminate multi-path distortion.

Who will provide technical or other engineering information on ILR stations and their reception?

The IBA Engineering Information Service, 70 Brompton Road, London SW3 1EY (telephone 01-584 7011 extension 444) will be glad to give advice and information on the ILR stations. ●

"Loudspeakers are like human beings; you need to live with them in order to detect their weaknesses."

Donald Aldous, former recording engineer, is now a well known technical journalist and audio consultant and has won the "Hi-Fi Journalist of the Year" Award (1972). Author of the first *"Manual of Direct Disc Recording"* (1943) and contributor to the world's hi-fi magazines, he is also Founder Member No. 1 of the British Sound Recording Association (1936), and a member of many technical organizations. His special interest is tape recording, and he is President of South Devon Tape Recording Club. Now Technical Editor of HI-FI NEWS & RECORD REVIEW he has many broadcasts on audio and record topics for BBC3 to his credit.

The loudspeaker is the last link in the audio chain—if the listening room and the ear are excluded—and this familiar device converts electrical impulses into sound waves, hence it is sometimes referred to as a *transducer*.

The modern loudspeaker unit consists of a permanent magnet, and a cone or diaphragm on which is mounted a coil of wire—usually copper or aluminium—known as the speech or voice coil, through which the signal currents are passed from the amplifier output terminals.

With no signals or current flowing, the coil remains stationary in the annular gap between the magnet pole pieces. When currents from the amplifier, that is, programme material, circulate in the coil a magnetic field is created in opposition to the steady magnetic field of the permanent magnet. Thus the coil moves and its linked cone with it. This electromagnetic force, known from one's school physics, when fed from the alternating current signals will cause the cone/coil combination to follow these to-and-fro movements. In turn these will create air pressure variations in front of and behind the cone.

Thus it can be seen that the generation of sound waves depends upon alternate compressions and rarefactions—partial vacuums one might say—of the air distributed into the listening area.

If the sound source is an unmounted loudspeaker unit, as its cone moves forward, it creates a compression wave in front of it. Simultaneously, the back surface of the cone is producing a comparable rarefaction. In an effort to equalize the sound pressure, the compressed air leaks around the edge of the cone, and the net result is a 'cancellation' effect, the extent of which varies according to the frequency, being specially severe at the bass frequencies. At high frequencies, the faster oscillation of the cone means that the air does not have time to travel between front and back, so the cancellation effect is less significant.

The solution to this problem is to mount the loudspeaker on a 'baffle' board, thus increasing the distance the air has to travel to cause cancellation or interference. Down to a frequency of 120 Hz. or so, fitting a baffle board of about 36 inches wide will suffice; below that

7 Loudspeakers and room acoustics

by Donald Aldous

Small, bookshelf loudspeakers are increasingly popular and are capable of high quality sound reproduction.

frequency the baffle becomes bigger and bigger until it is impractical for domestic use.

Infinite baffles

Thus, the so-called IB or 'infinite baffle' was born. Theoretically, if the isolating baffle could be made large enough, we would have an 'infinite baffle', but in practice the answer is found in 'folding' the original flat baffle into a box of reasonable dimensions. However, the enclosure or cabinet thus made brings its own problems, as now the rear of the cone is working against the air trapped in the box. This air acts as a spring, raising the natural vibrating frequency or 'fundamental resonance' of the particular unit into its operating range, producing the so-called 'one note bass' sound.

This effect is controlled by lining the enclosure with damping or sound absorbing material and increasing the size of the enclosure. In the early days of high fidelity when only one loudspeaker was necessary for monophonic sound, an enclosure as big as 10 cubic feet was not uncommon. In those early days, some experimenters—with a suitable domestic environment and an amenable lady of the household—mounted the loudspeaker unit in a wall between two rooms or cut a hole in the floorboards to mount the unit, when the space below the floor was hollow and large.

There are, however, other ways of tackling the problem of the bass resonance. Firstly, the cone suspension may be softened, and this will also allow the cabinet size to be reduced somewhat. Secondly, the cone itself may be made of heavier and stiffer material, but this will require a more powerful magnet or the use of an amplifier of a higher output power rating, since the electro-acoustic efficiency, or its sensitivity looked at another way, will be reduced.

Because the stiff, heavier cone will not reproduce the higher frequencies a 'tweeter', too, will have to be added. Lastly, a small cone unit may be mounted in a small cabinet, but this solution will impose severe restrictions on the lowest frequency that can be efficiently radiated.

Since energy losses in IB enclosures are considerable, being dissipated mainly as heat, and exacerbated by reduced box size, it is often necessary to employ a fairly powerful amplifier to drive such systems.

Totally sealed IB boxes can strictly be termed 'sealed enclosures' if not true infinite baffles. So we come to the other methods of bass loading, the so-called 'acoustic suspension' designs (a term and the principle coined by the American firm Acoustic Research), in which the enclosure is small enough so that the contained air serves as an integral element of the speaker cone mounting assembly. The drive units have high compliance (low stiffness) cones mounted on a loose rim suspension permitting larger cone movement for a given electrical power input. Thus, the free air resonant frequency decreases with the increase in cone mounting compliance.

This type of enclosure must be heavily lagged with sound absorbent materials, often to the extent of filling

Loudspeakers come in a wide range of shapes and sizes. Listening is the only way to make a final choice for your room.

the box completely with a suitable substance, such as close-packed fibre glass, cotton-wool, soft felt, bonded acetate fibre, etc. The resonant frequency can be shifted up and down the scale by an appropriate alteration of the interior volume of the enclosure, and so the designer has to achieve an acceptable combination of the loudspeaker elements and enclosure for a good overall performance.

Efficiency

The popularity of the small 'bookshelf' loudspeaker, as exemplified in the acoustic suspension system, is likely to increase, despite its low efficiency (or sensitivity). The coming of quadraphony, bringing with it the necessity of fitting four loudspeakers into the room, is likely to result in an increasing demand for speakers of this type. When not properly designed, they may introduce boomy, muddy bass, but this need not be so. And beware that one's room is not contributing to this 'colouration'.

Apart from the IB types, other methods of bass loading include the acoustic labyrinth and 'transmission line', in which the pressure waves from the rear of the drive cone flow down a long tunnel lined with absorbent material until at the open end no signal remains to cancel the front signal.

Bass reflex designs

In this method, the back radiation from the cone is delayed sufficiently by the spring effect of the air in the enclosure to emerge in phase with (i.e. adding to) the front or wanted signal, through a carefully dimensioned port or hole. To avoid distortion and inadequate power handling, this type of vented cabinet needs careful matching of enclosure and drive unit. The effect of a

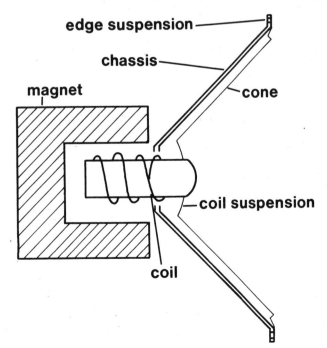

Fig. 1: Basic diagram of moving coil loudspeaker drive unit, showing main features.

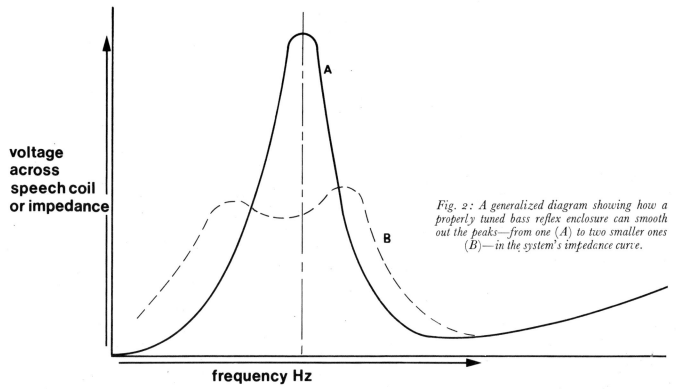

voltage across speech coil or impedance

frequency Hz

Fig. 2: A generalized diagram showing how a properly tuned bass reflex enclosure can smooth out the peaks—from one (A) to two smaller ones (B)—in the system's impedance curve.

properly tuned reflex cabinet in spreading the big resonant peak over two smaller humps, leading to a smoother bass response, is shown in the accompanying gdiaram.

Horn loading

Horn loading is the most efficient type of loudspeaker mounting, and this is supported by the fact that cinema sound systems employ horns. Admittedly, the sound output drops below a frequency dependent on the rate of taper and the horn mouth area, which may involve lengths of 10 to 20 feet or greater, and several square feet of mouth flare. (See the accompanying diagram for the names and different rates of flare.) A few dedicated audiophiles—mostly bachelors—have built such monsters under the floor boards of their listening rooms, but the only practicable constructional form for most homes is a folded split horn to reduce the overall dimensions, although it is still quite large and fits best in the corner of a big room.

It is possible to produce a very good loudspeaker fitted only with a single driver, but the design problems are eased by using two or more units, each handling only part of the audio frequency band. In such an assembly, the 'woofer' handles the lower audio frequencies up to, say, 1 kHz.; the 'squawker' or mid-range reproducer covers

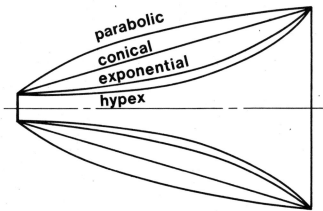

Fig. 3: The different shapes and rates of flare used in the design of loudspeaker horns.

about 200 to 4,000 Hz.; and the 'tweeter' is a high frequency unit for the range above 2 kHz. These frequencies vary, of course, with the designs, and there is overlap. Supertweeters are made for some systems, with further division of the upper frequency band and 'crossover' frequencies at, say, 4,500 and 12,000 Hz. The operating principle of the drive units in this range may be the familiar moving-coil (fitted with a small inflexible dome or diaphragm), or employ a ribbon, ionic or electrostatic unit.

Diaphragms

Diaphragms (cones) for loudspeakers used to be made from paper (suitably coated to avoid humidity effects), but over the years various materials have been tried, from the 'sandwich' construction of polystyrene coated on both sides with aluminium, to the bass unit with a flat polystyrene oval surface covered with an aluminium skin. Other modern materials include Melinex, a plastic used for domed treble units, and Bextrene, a rubber modified polystyrene material treated with a PVC layer. The old big magnets have given way to ceramic materials (such as, barium ferrite) and synthetic rubbers (like Neoprene) are finding favour for suspension assemblies.

Electrostatic loudspeaker

The most popular of the unorthodox designs is the ELS or electrostatic unit which, although fundamentally non-linear, by the development of a push-pull driving system with a substantially constant charge, has made it possible to manufacture not only high-frequency radiators, but 'full range' designs of genuine high-fidelity performance.

The most widely known version of this type yet realized is the Acoustical Manufacturing Company's QUAD model. Although its physical appearance does not lend itself to all room decors or personal tastes, its clinical clarity of sound and freedom from any 'boxy' colouration, when fed from the right system (as stringent amplifier specifications are demanded) make it still a standard of comparison for many audiophiles, amateur or professional.

This type of ELS system is known as a 'doublet'

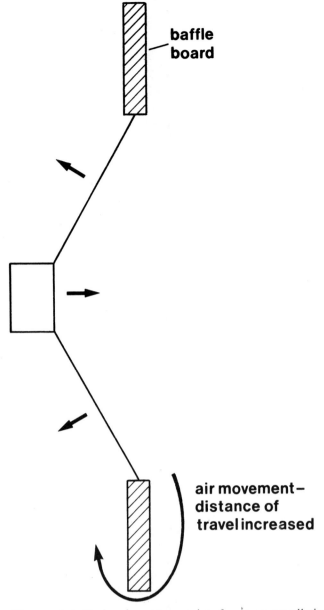

baffle board

air movement – distance of travel increased

Fig. 4: A baffle board can prevent interference or cancellation effects, except at the lowest frequencies.

because it radiates sound both to the front and rear, and it does not require experimenting to find the best place for it in any given room. A mains supply is needed to operate it.

A term that may be encountered when examining loudspeaker specifications is 'monitor' types. Strictly it should be restricted to high-grade professional designs (often with inbuilt amplifiers and complex equalization networks to contour the overall response), but it is now being attached to any loudspeaker system that the manufacturer considers to be of high quality. No specification is very widely accepted, other than the high performance BBC design in its commercial forms employed by various broadcasting organizations for 'monitoring' programmes.

Crossover Networks

In loudspeaker systems using more than one unit, it is necessary for each unit to receive signals only for the frequency range it was designed to handle. Thus, if a strong low frequency signal is fed to a small high frequency unit, the latter will be pushed to the limit of its travel, thereby causing distortion. Again, if a high frequency signal reaches the bass unit, the periphery of the cone

cannot follow the drive from the centre, and so introduces distortion.

The allocation of bands of frequencies to each unit is performed by a dividing network, and the points at which it selects each speaker are called 'crossovers'. These networks can be simple dividing circuits, called quarter or half section crossover filters, or they can be complicated and expensive networks involving bandpass filters and various damped resonant circuits.

Column speakers

Yet another style loudspeaker configuration (for low frequency loading) is the column design, which was popular some years ago when stereo was young. Its advantages included the small floor space—not more than 1 ft. square usually taken up, and the radiation of sound at a height above furniture. Many enthusiasts with limited space stood them behind glassware cabinets or bookcases in corners.

Omni-directional speakers

Yet another type of loudspeaker is known as 'omni-directional', in which the sounds are distributed all round, and so obviates the one-position 'stereo seat'. Some designers consider that the ideal 360° loudspeaker will be of this type, but the sounds should come from direct radiating units and not from reflective surfaces, as in one Swedish model.

If you are a DIY audio enthusiast, the several loudspeaker kits on the market will have an appeal to you, as such home construction projects require carpentry knowledge more than electronics. But if you are primarily interested in the end product—musical sounds—and not the means, the complete packaged system is what you need. In this way the problem of matching amplifiers to suitable loudspeakers, and finding or making up the correct leads and plugs for interconnection, is solved from the moment of purchase, as all these items are included in the package.

Budget hi-fi

Budget hi-fi systems can start as low as £75 or so, but obviously at this price, the loudspeakers will be single unit models in small enclosures. Often the drive unit will be a 7 in. by 5 in. elliptical type in a box, but going up the price scale, compact systems often sold in matched pairs can be bought for £35 or so. These may contain an 8 in. bass unit, with a 3 in. pressure unit, and a simple crossover network. For around £60 per pair, a bigger cabinet speaker, fitted with a passive bass radiator (which augments the output of the bass unit), plus three units, including a ¾ in. diaphragm tweeter are available.

Another combination is two 8 in. bass units with a 1 in. dome tweeter—this is seen in the Ekco Type 5427 system—

and the Type DX 321 loudspeaker assembly employs one 10 in. unit, two 5 in. units and a 1 in. dome tweeter. These models have a power rating of 35 watts and are available with the Ekco-Pye ZU9 Unit Audio system.

Even more sophisticated and expensive designs might house three units handling the bass notes, the middle range, and then the ultra-high frequency register (up to 25,000 Hz.), which, although requiring an elaborate dividing network, may not be too bulky in size these days. Usually these speakers are produced in teak, walnut or white finishes to blend with any surroundings.

Choosing loudspeaker system

By now it will have been appreciated that loudspeakers are marketed in a diversity of designs—big ones, small ones, fat ones, thin ones, squat ones, slim ones, round ones, square ones, and in a variety of colours. The newest style for the home is the flat 'sound panel', made of polystyrene material supported in a rugged, wooden frame which can be hung on a wall.

In the final analysis, a listening test, and preferably an A–B side-by-side switchover comparison is the only way to make a choice, subjective as it may be. Try to arrange this in your own listening room, as a home trial under relaxed conditions can avoid disappointment. Listen for colouration, lack of smoothness, poor balance and abrupt changes in directivity with slight head movements. Put another way, this means that the two main criteria are a reasonably high efficiency at low frequencies, and a fairly consistent polar response (directional response).

As no two listening rooms are alike in size, shape or acoustics, you may well have to play around with the positioning of the loudspeakers within the listening area to find the most satisfying arrangement.

Living with loudspeakers

Don't just audition with 'pop' music records or radio when evaluating results. Try to hear some speech (which should sound natural and not boomy), string tone (not wiry or screechy), soprano voice, percussive piano sounds for freedom from rattle, an organ for bass tones, and a full orchestra or operatic extracts with wide dynamics and complex harmonic structure to test the loudspeaker to its limits. Like human beings, one really needs to live with loudspeakers to detect their weaknesses, so first impressions can be wrong. What most music-lovers want, in the long run, is non-fatiguing musical sound that pleases the ear over an extended period of listening.

Try to get a speaker that makes sounds like the real thing, for that is 'high fidelity'.

Installation

Ordinary twisted twin-wire 5 amp. lighting flex can be used for loudspeaker connections, or similar grade— known as 14/0076 gauge twin—flat wire, and no special safety requirements are necessary, as the voltage on the lines is small. However, whiskers on wire ends that short circuit can damage transistor amplifiers, or at least blow the protective fuses, if fitted, so make the LS connections properly, but switch off the amplifier before interfering with the wiring and plugs. If speaker leads need to be run over 40 feet or so, it would be wise to employ a thicker gauge wire to keep the resistance down.

Don't worry too much about mismatching impedances between amplifier and loudspeakers, if only slight. This will have substantially no effect on quality, only on power transfer. However, this may be important when using low power amplifiers (less than 10 watts, say) with low efficiency speakers, if you want a reasonable sound level free of distortion.

Phasing

Power handling capacity of the loudspeakers should be at least that of the maximum output of each channel of the amplifier, although this volume level may never be used for any length of time. Most transistors amplifiers offer a wide range of output impedances, usually from 4 to 16 ohms. Power output is generally highest when feeding the lower figure, but there are advantages in using the higher value. The widely adopted compromise today is a nominal 8 ohms.

In any multiple loudspeaker system it is necessary to

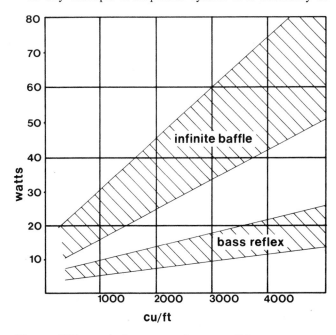

Fig. 5: This graph shows approximate amplifier power output requirements for rooms of various dimensions and for two different types of loudspeaker—IB and bass reflex.

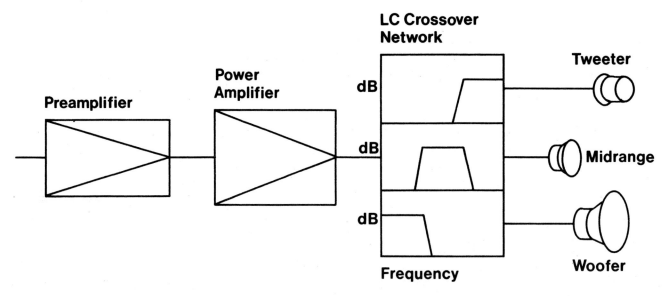

Fig. 6: Both three-way—as shown here—and two-way crossover networks are in common use to divide the frequency spectrum into right units. Only the best components and circuits must be used to avoid distortion, so such networks can be expensive.

ensure that the units are electrically 'phased', or a lack of 'presence' or poor localization of the centre image (of stereo pair) will be apparent. To check the phasing of two stereo speakers, play a mono record or radio programme (preferably speech) through them, and change over the lead connections to one of the loudspeakers only, not both, a few times, and listen for the arrangement that gives maximum bass. This is the correct in-phase method and the terminals or leads should be identified in some way. Different coloured leads are useful here. If you have any difficulty in detecting the connections that put the signals in phase, place the speaker cabinets close together and then listen. Some manufacturers mark their terminals with a coloured dot to show phase, and a standard code would help. The DIN non-reversible two-pin plug (one round pin and one flat pin) for loudspeaker connections is a useful system now widely adopted.

Loudspeaker positioning

Placing loudspeakers in the best position in the listening room is still a matter of trial and error, but the procedure can be helped by a few comments on the reasons why speaker placement affects the resultant sounds. Corner location does provide maximum bass, but in this position more reflections are introduced and room resonances excited, which can cause 'boomy' distortion in small rooms. Try moving the speakers about a few feet in various directions until they sound better to you. (See section on **Room acoustics.**)

Standing the loudspeaker cabinet directly on the floor can produce a bass boost—from reflections—and cause a 'heavy' sound. Remember too, that the high-frequency unit (tweeter) should be at about ear height, when seated in one's listening chair, and not firing into a settee or other furniture. It is desirable to have the speaker raised some 6 inches or so off the floor, not on a box, but with free air under it. This is standard practice with modern 'monitor' loudspeakers, which are usually mounted on a stand.

Try to place the loudspeakers about 7 to 12 feet apart and experiment with the positions shown in the diagram, but you may find some other layout preferable. If it sounds good to you, that's fine. Well designed 'omni' loudspeakers radiate high frequencies in practically all directions (from reflectors or the use of many small units)

with the bass woofer spreading sound in all directions, which presentation can please some listeners and room conditions, but the stereo picture is not so precisely located.

The quality of stereo headphones has improved vastly in recent years, and models are now available in many shapes and sizes with a performance comparable to loudspeakers in a much higher price bracket.

Headphone listening

Headphones offer intimate personal listening, as a matter of necessity to enjoy sound at high levels without disturbing others watching television, say, or disturbing children sleeping or neighbours late at night, or as a matter of convenience to avoid room acoustic problems and get true high fidelity performance at an economic price. The anti-social aspect of private listening can be overcome by using several pairs of headsets connected via a distribution/switch box.

Listening through stereo headphones is actually 'binaural' and not strictly stereophonic as from loudspeakers, with each ear getting sounds from *both* loudspeakers. In fact, the 'sound stage' seems to be within one's head or sometimes passes through one's head and moves around with the head. A so-called 'blend' circuit or 'dimension control' to mix the right and left hand channels to a certain extent offsets this problem, if the listener is bothered by this psycho-acoustic phenomenon of earphone listening, as opposed to 'free-field' listening.

Most users are more likely to be bothered by comfort and the weight of headsets than spatial effects in the reproduction. Today a big selection of headphones is on the market; most of these are moving-coil types, but the electrostatic designs offer superb quality at a higher price. Another design is known as Isodynamic.

With no universal standard for headphone impedances or sensitivity ratings yet, it is advisable to match the headphones approximately to the other equipment. The impedance values can vary from 8 to 200 ohms, say, to 600 ohms or more, and the headphone sockets of some equipment may well be for low impedance types. Direct connection of headsets across loudspeakers outputs is not satisfactory, as the amplifier volume control has to be set very low introducing noise problems. The signal has to be attenuated by inserting resistors, of suitable value, in series with the headphone wiring. If in any doubt about

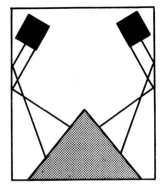
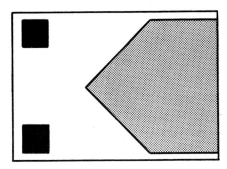
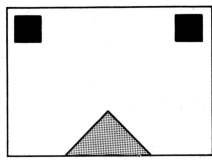

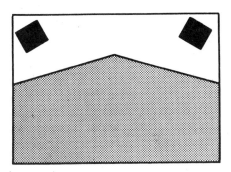
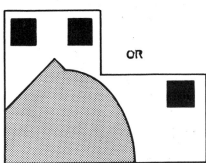
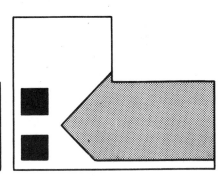

Fig. 7: Suggested stereo loudspeaker positions in listening rooms of different shapes. The largest listening areas are shown shaded. The L-shaped room (bottom centre) has two arrangements, which can be assessed by trial to find the preferred layout, and yet another placing is seen in the bottom right-hand plan.

impedances, or connections, consult your dealer.

Room boundaries obviously have an effect on the bass performance of loudspeakers, as does the position of the loudspeaker in relation to the walls. For example, if the speaker were suspended in the centre of a large room, the sound output would be spread over a sphere. Placing the speaker on the floor it radiates into a hemisphere, and doubles the efficiency. If the speaker is stood against a flat wall, the volume into which the sound is radiated is again reduced, and the efficiency improved. Finally, by placing the speaker in a corner of the room, it radiates into only one-eighth of a sphere producing the most bass output, particularly impressive with horn loaded types.

Room acoustics

The overall acoustic character of a room (due to furnishings, curtains, carpets, apart from shape and size) does influence the tonal quality and balance of reproduced sound. In fact, two loudspeakers with substantially identical specifications may sound quite different, according to the surroundings in which they are played.

Room resonances (so-called *eigentones*) are produced by parallel walls in a room, and so a cube-shaped room makes the worst shape for listening, as does one that is nearly twice as long as it is wide. The best dimensions—for medium rooms—follow the so-named Golden Ratio: 1:1.6:2.5 and for small rooms, try a ratio of 1:1.25:1.6

for Height, Width and Length. This compromise means a room, for instance, measuring 8 ft. 6 ins. by 10 ft. 6 ins. by 13 ft. 6 ins. which staggers the room resonances. Deep alcoves, even bay windows, and non-parallel walls are useful to reduce this resonance effect.

The 'perfect' loudspeaker

Can the 'perfect' loudspeaker be made, as the hundreds of speakers so far available all appear to have their own 'house' sound, which differences must mean that they are imperfect? Even the latest and most advanced designs, for example, the new Philips 'motional feedback' concept with its inbuilt amplifier in the speaker cabinet controlling distortion in the bass driver, does not make such a claim. Unquestionably, though, loudspeakers in this category offer a most satisfying hi-fi sound, although the search for the ideal transducer will go on.

Some designers believe that the so-called 'pulsating sphere' made up of multiple units, if all external conditions were equal, might achieve this goal, but don't delay buying the best current loudspeakers you can afford, bearing in mind the room dimensions and acoustics, not to mention family requirements. Although now a cliché, the final arbiter must be your ears, and what you hear and like is exclusive to you. To keep your ears 'clean' though, listening to the sounds at a 'live' performance is the only worthwhile standard of comparison. ●

"Tape machines? Take your pick from reel-to-reel, cassette or cartridge."

Basil Lane is Assistant Editor of WIRELESS WORLD, having joined the staff in 1972. Trained originally as a technician apprentice in the Post Office, he spent some time in the field as a maintenance engineer and then transferred to the Post Office Training Centre at Bletchley as an Instructor. It was there that he developed an interest in journalism and hi-fi equipment design, this growing over several years during which he transferred again to the Post Office Research Laboratories. Over the past three years he has gained considerable practical experience in the design and servicing of cassette and tape recorders through operating a consulting company.

For many of us there are several considerations involved in the purchase of a tape recorder and these can be listed quite simply as follows.

1. Purchase price and running costs.
2. Facilities offered and recording/reproducing quality.
3. Styling and size.

Within the unit audio range, most demands can be met by making a careful comparison of products and discussing some of the more technical problems with your dealer. In the next few pages, I hope to explain a few of the factors that affect the first two considerations.

There are three types of tape machine in common domestic use, the reel-to-reel (sometimes called the open reel) machine, the cassette machine, and the cartridge machine. The essential differences are as follows:-

The Open Reel Recorder uses tape $\frac{1}{4}$in wide which comes in various lengths and thicknesses and is wound on spools of various diameters. The speed that the tape passes through the machine can be selected, in most machines, from a range of fixed values which give either higher standards of recording and reproduction, or economy of tape.

Such a recorder usually offers comprehensive recording facilities in either mono or stereo, or a combina-

8
Tape recorders – the cassette for home and car

by Basil Lane

tion. Because of the accessibility and relative ease of handling of the tape, splicing (jointing) can be undertaken enabling programmes to be edited. Usually the tape can be recorded in two directions of travel to double the recording time, thus it would first wind from the left reel to the right and then the reels are reversed and turned over to record on the second half of

the tape width. There are no commercially recorded music tapes available in Europe and the U.K. thus confining its use exclusively to recording enthusiasts. Almost all open reel recorders are mains powered though there are a few exceptions, but these tend to be expensive semi-professional machines powered by rechargable batteries.

Cassette recorders use $\frac{1}{8}$in wide tape

which is wound in a miniature reel-to-reel form inside a small plastic case. This type of machine is very simply loaded by just inserting the cassette into a suitably designed chamber in the cassette recorder. The tape runs through the machine at a single speed of $1\frac{7}{8}$in/s (4.75cm/s), and is available in various lengths, these being indicated by the total recording time printed as a simple code on the cassette label, e.g. C30=30 mins, C60=60 mins, etc.

The cassette can be played in both directions, usually by turning it over, but in some instances in modern and very expensive machines this is either achieved by an automatic reverse facility, or some similar device. Machines are made for mono or stereo but unlike the open reel recorder, recordings made on a stereo-only machine can be played back on a mono-only machine. Most cassette recorders have some simple recording facilities, a few are playback only.

There is a vast range of commercially duplicated music cassettes available through record dealers, making this type of machine a useful adjunct to a record player. Cassette recorders are to be found as battery portables, mains powered, or even designed to be fitted into a car. Since the basic mechanism is small and the associated

Fig. 1 : A typical domestic tape recorder.

electronics relatively simple, some cassette recorders are to be found in combination with amplifiers, record players or tuners. In such an arrangement, the complexities of inter-connection of units is eliminated and recording from these sources simplified to the operation of one or two buttons.

Since these recorders have a low tape speed, considerably greater manufacturing expertise is required to make machines capable of the same order of performance as the open reel machine. However, remarkably high performance can be found in some quite reasonably priced products.

The Cartridge recorder was invented in America and is most popular there and in Japan. It uses ¼in tape enclosed in a plastic case somewhat larger than the cassette and wound as an endless loop. Tape speed is 3¾in/s (9.5cm/s). Almost all machines are designed for playback only, although a few for home use include record facilities.

Most machines on the market are intended for in-car entertainment and can play mono, stereo or sometimes four channel recordings. Commercially duplicated music cartridges are available, although the system has not proved to be as popular as the cassette which generally offers a wider variety of applications.

For most, choosing between these types starts by considering the case for cassette versus open reel machine. In very basic terms, this can be summarized by saying that the open reel machine offers most to the *recording* enthusiast, the cassette recorder largely for the playback enthusiast, although, as we shall see, quite a lot can still be undertaken using the cassette recorder. Of course, within these two classes of machine there is a range of quality and facilities which remain to be investigated.

The open reel recorder

Fig. 1 is an illustration of a high quality tape recorder suitable for integration with a Unit Audio System. It has a wide range of recording facilities typical of a modern stereo machine. There are more complex machines with an even higher performance and also cheaper versions of greater simplicity, but the essential features of all open reel machines can be recognised in this product.

Tape for this machine comes wound on various diameter reels in a selection of lengths and thicknesses. The table which follows gives typical tape lengths for the various reel dia-

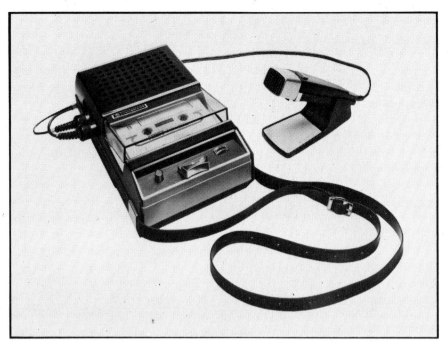

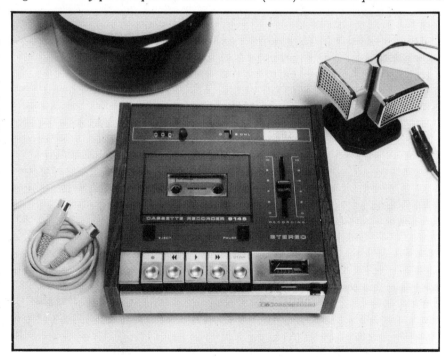

Fig. 2: A battery-powered portable cassette recorder (above) and a mains-powered machine.

meters most often available and for different thicknesses of tape.

Your dealer will give you some idea of the cost of the various types of tape, but this will not give the complete information required to calculate running costs. The reason for this is that the actual amount of tape used, will depend upon the tape speed selected. Open reel recorders can usually be operated at one of several standard speeds, these being 1⅞in/s (4.75cm/s); 3¾in/s (9.5cm/s); and 7½in/s (19cm/s). Higher tape speeds can be found in

Table One

Reel dia.	Length and type of tape		
3in	LP = 210ft	DP = 300ft	TP = 450ft
5in	= 900ft	= 1200ft	= 1800ft
7in	= 1800ft	= 2400ft	= 3600ft

Modern 'electronic developments have so miniaturized the equipment needed for amplifiers that very compact units are available, needing only the addition of speakers for full stereo reproduction.

In these integrated ready-to-use players, all items, including speakers, are balanced at the design stage and there is no risk of one weak component reducing sound quality below the potential of the rest of the equipment.

Running time	Tape length in ft at a speed of		
	$1\frac{7}{8}$in/s	$3\frac{3}{4}$in/s	$7\frac{1}{2}$in/s
10 mins	93.75	187.5	375
30 mins	281.25	562.5	1125
1 hour	562.5	1125	2250

Fig. 3: An I.C.E. (in car entertainment) cassette player (top), a radio/cassette recorder (centre), and a ZU5K combination.

semi-professional and studio applications. The running time for various tape lengths is given in the table, left.

It is easily concluded from these tables that the thinner tapes offer many advantages in terms of recording time. There is, however, a point of caution that should be made. The thinner tapes are much more susceptible to damage during handling; this means that if the recording requires editing or is to be subjected to a lot of use, then the thicker DP or LP tapes will prove to be more satisfactory.

Track configurations

Recorded tape looks no different from blank tape—there is no visible evidence of change. In fact as is inferred by the name, the change produced by recording is a magnetic one. The tape carries a coating of extremely small particles rather like very small bar magnets. The action of recording changes the random magnetisation of these miniature magnets into a coherent pattern which becomes finer in its detail, the higher the frequency or note recorded.

Since the full width of the tape is not needed to give good recording quality, it can be divided into two or more "tracks" which can be used for mono or stereo recording. Fig. 4 shows the location of these recorded tracks for different types of machine and also shows the direction of tape travel when those particular tracks are being recorded or replayed. Alongside are drawings of the recording or replay heads showing the location of the recording and pick-up cores. By comparing these drawings and noting the relative position of tracks and cores, it will be seen that tapes recorded on some types of machine cannot be replayed on others. The most important point to get over is that the tracks are created by the recorder and are not on the tape when it is purchased.

Track selection

On many recorders there are switches on the control panel. This makes it possible preferentially to select to record or playback on one or more tracks. Normal track numbering is from the top edge of the tape to the bottom, so on a four track machine the record and replay heads can be switched to operate on track one (four in the reverse direction) or three, (two in the reverse direction).

With separate record and replay heads it is also possible to monitor the quality of the actual recording on the tape as it is being made. However, on cheaper machines, only one head is used to serve both record and replay functions and so in this case it is impossible to monitor directly off tape. In some cases, track selection can be accomplished in slightly different ways to obtain either "duoplay" or "multiplay" facilities. In duoplay, a mono recording can be made, first on track one. This can be replayed whilst recording say, an accompaniment on track 3.

In multiplay, this same process can be repeated a number of times by shifting the gradually built up recording from track 1 to track 3 and then back, adding on one more recording each time.

Erasing

Magnetic tape has a considerable advantage over more mechanical systems of recording in that it can be "wiped clean" and used again. All new tapes come in this condition, the erasing having been done in bulk during the manufacturing stage. However, the recorder itself has an erase head which, when the recorder is switched into the record mode, will automatically wipe clean those areas or tracks which are to be recorded on. This means that in the duoplay or multiplay modes some sections of the erase head are turned off to prevent a previous recording from disappearing before it has been replayed.

Mixing

In making a recording, most people like to produce a professional polish to the final tape. Most of us take as an example, the sort of effects produced by broadcast stations. The most familiar of these techniques is to "talk over", where voice announcements are mixed with music. Another facility is smoothly to fade from one music source to another.

Tape recorders have facilities to do this sort of thing because separate inputs are available for microphones, and amplifiers. These in turn, could have another tape recorder and a record turntable connected. Thus, using the separate level controls for each recorder input a balance can be struck between two signal sources to give talk-over or cross-fading.

Selecting the recording level

In some ways, magnetic tape is rather like the ear, too low a volume or level and the sound becomes inaudible and too high a level and the ear hurts due to the overload. It is

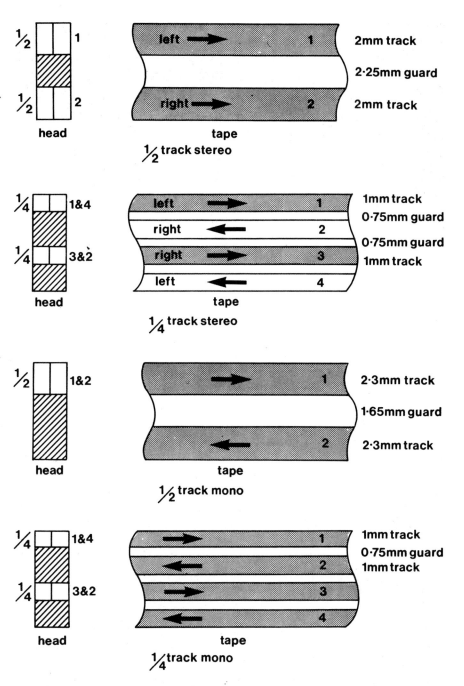

Fig. 4: The track pattern and head layout of an open reel machine.

important therefore, to ensure that recordings are made in a way that ensures against overload on the one hand and the music disappearing on the other!

A most convenient way of achieving this is to use a VU (volume unit) meter which continuously measures the level of signal being recorded. Sometimes the meter is also connected to the playback—a fact that is not of much use except in cases where a tape needs evaluating. Most open reel and cassette recorders are fitted with one or two VU meters. If only one is found on a stereo machine it is usually arranged to read the highest signal in either left or right channels automatically.

Because the needle movement is

slow compared to the speed of changes in loudness of the music, it is possible that the meter will fail to register extremely short, high level bursts of sound and some care has to be taken in setting record levels to avoid this. Wherever possible the needle should not be allowed to enter the red zone to the right of the zero mark.

In many of the expensive cassette recorders (and some of the open reel types) an automatic level setting circuit will, when switched on, look after unexpected overloads by turning the volume down during the high level section. It is best used and set up, by setting the levels on the meter with the circuit switched out, and then switching it in to cope with the un-

MUSICAL DREAMLAND for young and old. Tapes and records by the thousands are available at this Oxford Street shop— as at other shops all over Britain—for pop, 'standard' and classical music-lovers alike.
Some 120,000,000 discs are pressed in Britain every year. Sales in the first half of 1972 alone totalled £21,782,000.

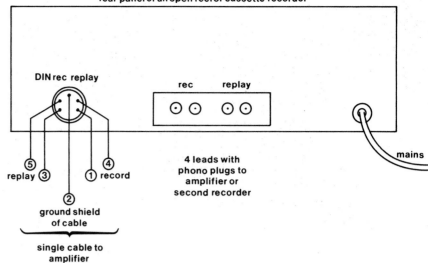

rear panel of an open reel or cassette recorder

DIN rec replay

rec   replay

5 replay 3   1 record 4

2

ground shield
of cable

single cable to
amplifier

4 leads with
phono plugs to
amplifier or
second recorder

mains

Fig. 5: A typical socket line-up for an open reel recorder.

expected. The switch controlling this circuit is marked with one of several sets of letters which are abbreviations of different terms, e.g. OLS (overload switch), AGC (automatic gain control), AVC (automatic volume control).

Cassette recorders

One of the most important basic characteristics of the cassette recorder is compatibility. This factor runs through all aspects of the system. For example, the dimensions of cassettes from all manufacturers should be the same within very close tolerances. Fig. 7 is a photograph of a typical cassette viewed from the front edge. Along the front edge are a series of holes designed to accommodate the erase head, the record/replay head and the pinch wheel. Also near the front top and bottom edges are holes which accept the capstan and the location pins which precisely position the cassette with respect to the recorder mechanism.

Looking at the rear edge of the cassette, there are two rectangular depressions partially covered in some cases by a plastic tab (in the case of new blank tapes). This is part of a "safety" mechanism, the rest of which is in the recorder. The mechanism operates if the tab is broken out and

prevents accidental erasure of a recording by locking the operation of the record button.

The reason for the difference in these "safety" holes as shown in Fig. 7 lies in the type of tape inside the cassette. The normal tape is coated with iron oxide particles (a very special form of rust) and the cassette has the smaller holes. A new type of tape using a coating based on chromium dioxide has recently appeared. This tape requires changes in the recorder electronics to produce optimum results. On some machines this is achieved with a manually operated switch marked CrO_2 and std (standard) but some later types have a switch operated by a feeler that senses the longer hole in the rear of CrO_2 cassettes.

In many respects, the cassette recorder can be considered to be just a very small reel-to-reel recorder, since the tape transport is similar and it can be made with the same sort of variations. For example, there are some very sophisticated machines with two or three motors to perform the various functions and even in some rare cases, machines have been manufactured with a separate monitor replay head. Perhaps the most useful asset of the system is that the cassette

itself is so small thus making it possible to make useful, portable machines that are very simple to operate. These cassette recorders contain additional amplifiers and a single loudspeaker. In almost all cases, portable cassette recorders are mono machines.

Unlike the open reel machine, all stereo cassette recordings are playable on a mono machine, the reason for this being almost self evident from Fig. 9. This drawing depicts the track patterns and head core arrangements for both mono and stereo operation. Clearly a mono head will scan both tracks of a stereo recording and, conversely, the two head cores of a stereo machine will scan almost all of the single track of a mono recording. This very convenient arrangement means that recordings made on portable mono machines can be replayed on the stereo mains powered machine often to be found integrated with a home Unit Audio system.

Music cassettes

Many record companies are now producing pre-recorded cassettes, almost always in stereo and providing for a wide range of tastes. In many cases, these cassettes are a duplication from the record catalogue.

Since the tape is well protected by

Fig. 6: The recording level meter (VU meter) used on most cassette and open reel recorders.

Fig. 7: A typical cassette showing the holes and mouldings on the front edge.

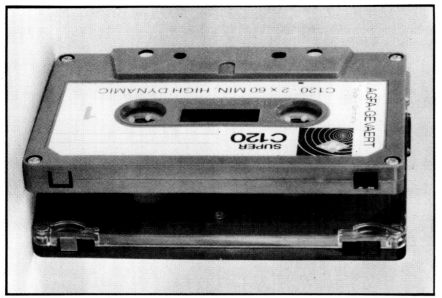

Fig. 8: A view of two types of cassette showing the "safety" tabs. One has been broken out to prevent recording over an existing recording. Note the different shaped holes on the chromium dioxide (lower) cassette.

its plastic case and the machines are simple to load and operate, the cassette recorder can be regarded as the answer to the prayer of a parent trying to protect his record collection and precious turntable from the ravages of his children!

In some instances, collectors have found the cassette a useful way of preserving old records, keeping the disc to generate new cassettes if they ever become damaged. However this sort of subject is best left to the section of this chapter that deals with the applications of the cassette recorder.

So far I have identified only two versions of the cassette recorder, the mains powered stereo machine designed to be combined with the Unit Audio system, and the mono portable. The diversity is in fact considerably greater than this since the cassette recorder mechanism lends itself well to combination with radio as a radio cassette recorder which is also portable.

Other combinations can be found for home use, where the cassette recorder is fitted in the same cabinet as the record player, amplifier and a tuner, thus providing a very versatile system.

The car cassette player is, perhaps, one of the most useful developments in the range of products available. Most people tend to think of "in-car-entertainment" (I.C.E.) in terms of the radio. The biggest limitation of that, however, is the pre-selection of programme by the broadcast station. With mono or stereo machines now available for simple fitting in the car, total self-determination of entertainment is possible. Cassettes recorded at home or those with commercial recordings, can be used in the car at will.

Recording facilities are sometimes provided on these machines making it possible to record favourite programmes off the car radio while travelling. Operation is absolute simplicity and with up to 60 minutes of programme on each side of the cassette, constant attention is unnecessary.

Recording with a cassette recorder

Almost all cassette recorders have some recording facilities, though these are nowhere near as comprehensive as those on the open reel machine. Those that can record will have a microphone socket at least, and are either supplied with one microphone, as in the case of most mono portables, or can be fitted with two, purchased as extras from your local dealer.

Again, most cassette recorders will have an input socket to permit connection to an amplifier making it possible to record from a disc or other source. The methods of connecting both cassette recorders and/or tape recorders to the Unit Audio system will be described in a later section.

Noise reduction: Dolby and DNL

Noise is around us everywhere, and although mostly it is of the unpleasant variety, sometimes it can be considered to be pleasant but is just unwanted sound spilling into our ears. A typical example would be the sound of the next-door-neighbours' radio wafting into your house at night! Unfortunately, apart from complaining we cannot do much to stop such noises, which is a pity, since they can spoil the pleasure of listening to good music.

All audio equipment adds its own noise to the signal it is reproducing and although it is mostly so low,

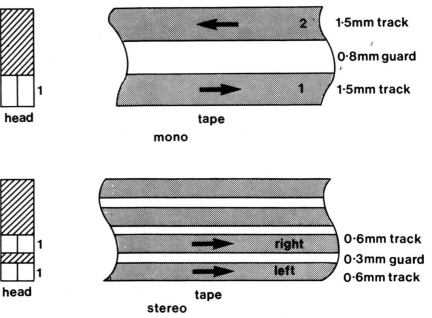

Fig. 9: The track pattern for cassette recorders shown with the head layout.

The tremendous force of the vibrations set up by a tuning fork are vividly demonstrated in this picture of a fork dipped into water immediately after being tapped.

Today's tape recorder is nothing if not versatile. Slung over a cameraman's shoulder, it can record faithfully—and effortlessly—the sounds of the countryside. It can help a mother and her child to keep in touch with loved ones at the other side of the world. It can be used, too, by busy men (and women) to tape on-the-spot reports for future reference.

compared to the signal, that it is not noticed, there are occasions when it can become obtrusive. Tape recorders tend to be worse in this respect, since the tape itself creates a steady noise which can degrade the music quality, especially if the sounds are very small. The actual amount of noise is, to a large extent, dependent upon the width of the recorded track and so it is obvious that cassette recorders will suffer rather more than open reel machines.

Two important methods have been developed to combat this problem and one or other will be found in many of the better quality recorders. The first, called the DNL (Dynamic Noise Limiter) was invented by Philips and is intended for use, either built in or as a separate plug-on "unit", with any noisy audio equipment—mostly cassette players.

It is a playback-only system and not used during recording, which means that it will operate satisfactorily with recordings made on any machine.

To appreciate just how noise reducers work, let us examine for a moment the nature of the noise itself. It is often referred to as tape hiss, not because all the noise is concentrated at the hiss (high frequency) end of the scale, but because our ears are most sensitive to those sorts of sounds. Noise becomes obtrusive only when the real sound we are trying to listen to, gets very small, so it can be said that a noise reducer is required only at these times.

All noise reducers for cassette recorders work, therefore, on the high frequencies and only during periods when the music signal is small. The Philips DNL can be likened to an automatic treble control. When the volume of wanted sound is high, the processer is out of the circuit and inoperative, but the lower the level of high frequencies, the more the treble is turned down, thus cutting off the noise which is gradually tending to become obtrusive. Considerable improvements can be made to the sound quality of low and medium priced equipment using this device.

For the medium and high priced cassette recorder, an alternative noise reduction system is offered, called the Dolby "B" process. Invented by Dolby Laboratories, it is again designed primarily for use with cassette recorders and will be found built into some machines, but can also be used in its "unit" form in a variety of other

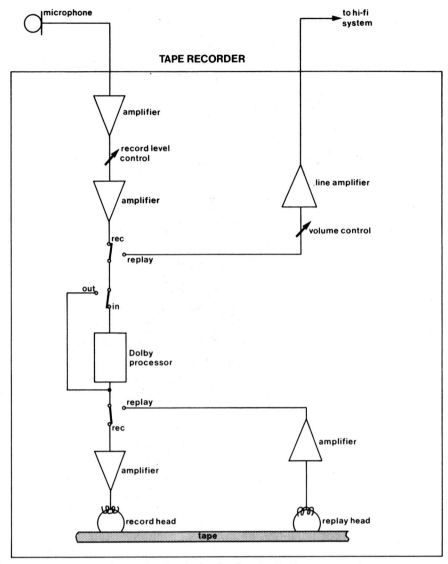

Fig. 10: Record/replay chain showing the Dolby processors in use.

situations. The principle difference between this and the DNL, is that it operates on both the recording and the replay chain. We can see just why when we refer to Fig. 10 which shows the signal from the microphone passing through the initial pre-amplifiers in the recorder and then being processed to boost the low level, high frequencies (whenever they occur).

The signal is then recorded on the tape, where most noise is added. Because there are now no low level, high frequencies, the noise remains separated from the music. On replay the process is reversed and the low level, high frequencies restored to their correct place, and incidentally the tape noise is also depressed to keep well below the recorded signal.

This is, of course, a highly simplified description of what happens. Since music levels can change rapidly and constantly, both systems are, when used, equally rapidly varying their level of operation to suit the conditions.

Because the Dolby process alters

the recording, such a cassette will sound different when replayed on a cassette recorder without Dolby. The effect is to give rather more treble—which can be cured by lowering the treble tone control a little. It also means that an altered sound will be produced if the Dolby is used to replay a cassette which has not been recorded with the Dolby process. For this reason, the circuit is provided with a switch to cut out the processor when not required.

Many commercially duplicated cassettes are now available, having been recorded using this process, and these are marked with the Dolby sign which looks like this.

There is no additional cost incurred for the commercially recorded cassettes and the quality improvements using this process and the DNL for all other material are well worth the investment.

So far we have been looking at the differences in facilities offered by cassette and open reel recorders. The next step is to show how it is possible to interpret some of the more important performance characteristics in order to be able to make value judgements when purchasing a new machine.

Performance specifications

The problem with these is that there is an inevitable dive into technical "jargon" that puzzles many and does not really contribute any useful knowledge. In addition, there is another rather odd technical difficulty of determining just how the measurements of performance should be made, since differences in method can produce different answers. Fortunately there is now a standard on which specifications are based called the DIN standard. It defines minimum requirements for tape recorders of all sorts and also lays down the dividing line between what they call the domestic recorder and the hi-fi recorder.

It was first introduced by the Germans but has been increasingly adopted by most equipment manufacturers. Thus, if ever you see a data sheet for a tape or cassette recorder which quotes figures "according to DIN 45511 or DIN 45500", at least you will know that the figures can be compared with those of any other machine for which the same specific claim has been made.

Unfortunately, there have been instances of the odd manufacturer trying to play some sort of numbers game and making use of questionable methods, or sometimes using other national standard specifications which help to produce better looking numbers. If you intend making use of the data given in the recorder specification, at least you should be aware of this occasional problem.

The table on the left gives the minimum requirements laid down by the two quoted DIN standards; reference should be made to the glossary where you are not sure of the meaning of any of the technical specifications.

What sort of cassette tape?

Although there is a wide variety of blank cassettes available it is well to be careful in their selection. The best for your machine will usually be that offered with the machine at the time of purchase—or recommended by the manufacturer. If no information is available then go for one of the large manufacturers brands which carry some guarantee of quality. Only use C120 cassettes if absolutely necessary as the tape is extremely delicate and can be easily damaged.

Most cassettes are of the iron-oxide tape type and their properties are similar. However, some advantages of improved performance are offered by chromium dioxide tape, which, if the machine is designed to accept it, bring better frequency response and signal-to-noise ratio.

An alternative suitable for use on standard cassette recorders is the so-called high energy tape which is more

Table Three

Parameter	DOMESTIC RECORDERS DIN 45511			HI-FI RECORDERS DIN 45500
	19cm/s	9.5cm/s	4.75cm/s	
Drift over 30 secs.	± 2%	± 2%	± 2%	± 1%
Wow and flutter	± 0.2%	± 0.3%	± 0.6%	± 0.2%
Frequency range f_1	40 Hz	63 Hz	80 Hz	40 Hz
(See drawing below) f_2	12.5 KHz	10 KHz	6.3 KHz	12.5 KHz
Signal-to-noise ratio	45dB	45dB	45dB	50dB
Crosstalk at 1 KHz mono	50dB	50dB	50dB	60dB
„ „ „ stereo	20dB	20dB	20dB	25dB
Distortion at max. record level at 333 Hz	5%	5%	5%	5%

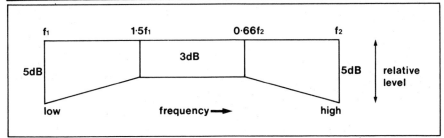

Before your very ears

Because of today's high standards of both recording and reproduction, the voices of top singers like Cliff Richard (right) and Cilla Black and Donovan (below) are faithfully reproduced in millions of homes all over Britain.

Microphones abound as Irish singer Dana (above) performs at an open-air concert in London's Hyde Park. One hand-microphone serves for Nana Mouskouri (right).

The singing strings of the Mantovani Orchestra are under the control of the baton of the maestro himself—one of Britain's biggest-selling recording artists.

expensive than the iron oxide type and brings only marginal advantages.

Care of tape and cassette recorders

This section deals not only with the care of the machine, but also the tapes themselves. There is a tendency to think that because tape recorders are built fairly solidly and seemingly have no really delicate components, compared with the record player, that maintenance is not really necessary. In fact this is not so, since regular cleaning is essential, if the original performance is to be preserved. Most dealers stock recorder cleaning kits and the use of these is preferable to any makeshift implements.

Nearly all the dirt that accumulates along the path of the tape is the result of debris shed from the tape itself. In some cases it is very resistant to cleaning operations and fluid is required to loosen it.

One of the safest of these is the detergent type specifically made for the tape recorder, although a useful alternative is Isopropyl Alcohol which can be obtained from the larger chemists shops. Particular attention should be paid first to the heads, since if dirt separates tape from head, then high frequency performance deteriorates rapidly. The next most important is the capstan and pinch wheel.

An accumulation of dirt on these can reduce friction on the tape causing an increase in the wow and flutter figures. Never, under any circumstances, use metal scrapers to clean the recorder, only the felt and cotton wool pads made for the job.

Lubrication is a necessary part of maintenance but is best undertaken by a qualified engineer. A recorder,

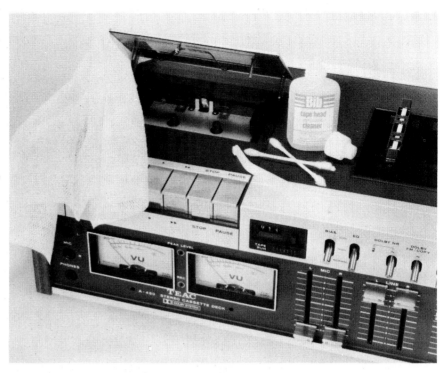

Fig. 11 : Cleaning the recorder with a popular cleaning kit.

just like a car, benefits from a service— say once every two years, when worn parts can be replaced and the machine brought back to its original standard of performance.

Storage of tapes

All modern audio tapes consist of a magnetic coating on a plastic foil. Heat will affect this plastic, particularly since it is very thin, and so storage conditions should be at room temperature and avoiding the extremes of humidity. Even more important, recordings should be kept away from strong magnets or magnetic fields. These can originate from powerful electric motors, loudspeakers, transformers—a component found in most audio equipment operated from the mains, and of course the magnetic

locks found on some furniture doors. These latter items are only dangerous to the recordings at close quarters and when the door is open.

Using open reel and cassette recorders

In this section, rather more emphasis is placed upon the cassette recorder, since it is more portable, and more popular. Already, the principle difference in the applications of these two types of recorder have been outlined. The open reel machine is for the serious hobbyist intent upon creative and fairly advanced recordings, while the cassette recorder is more suitable for simple recording situations with the added flexibility of using it as a convenient "notebook".

Since already there are several good

DOLBY: Dr. Ray Dolby, inventor of noise reduction systems. The Dolby "B" system is used in domestic equipment either as a built-in processor or as an add-on unit to convert existing equipment. Used with cassette and tape recorders, but has other applications not explored in Europe. Operation of the processor is described briefly as follows.

1. The signal to be recorded (music) is fed into the recorder input socket and can be described as a picture showing volume range and frequency range over a period of time. High notes tend to be low level and are more likely to be polluted by tape hiss.

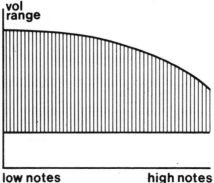

2. The Dolby B processor boost the high notes only whenever their volume is low.

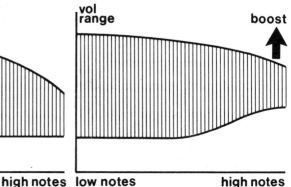

*Fig. 12: Devices suitable for demagnet-
ising the tape path of cassette, cartridge,
and open reel recorders.*

books on creative recording with an open reel machine, it is sufficent to say that most of its advantages arise from the ability to mix several sources of sound using the recording controls, and then to edit the tape to produce a very professional sounding result.

Editing, to remove mistakes or to change the order of several recordings in a reel of tape is done by a simple process of cutting and jointing.

Razor blades, used to trim or cut the tape should be very sharp to avoid producing ragged edges and the adhesive splicing tape should be of a type specially produced for the job. The main reason for being very particular on this point is that many of the popular stationery brands bleed adhesive after a period and thus, overlapping layers of tape could get

stuck together—or even worse—the tape could jam in the machine. Accessory splicing kits and leader tape, used to start and finish a reel, are readily available from most dealers.

Editing cassettes is an almost impossible job and so the most important prerequisite to a recording session using these machines is a careful planning of the final production. The hints and tips that follow are, in most cases, equally applicable to open reel recorders.

Connecting a cassette recorder for recording

We will assume that you already have a Unit Audio amplifier connected to a tuner and a record player. Connecting this amplifier to the cassette recorder for recording either from

this source, or from a microphone is shown in Fig. 13.

In simpler cassette recorders, the microphone and auxiliary sockets cannot be used simultaneously since the action of plugging in the amplifier disconnects the microphone. However, in the mains powered versions this is not usual.

Recording from the radio is fairly simple, with the record, play and pause buttons operated, the volume or record level control on the recorder should be set so that the VU meter needle flickers between −6 and 0; remembering that speech will usually be quieter than music.

Since broadcasting stations already regulate maximum sound levels very well, it should be possible to note the best average position for the record

3. The signal is then recorded on to the tape which adds its contribution of noise as drawn. The boosted high notes are kept clear of the noise.

4. On replay the Dolby "B" processor reverses its role to depress the high notes back to their former volume level, at the same time the noise, which is now part of the replayed signal is also depressed.

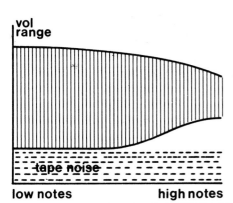

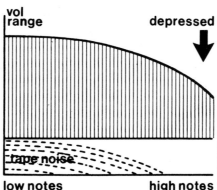

This processing is in a continual state of change with the actual degree of boost on record and depression on replay changing instantaneously to ensure that only the low level, high note signals receive maximum boost. Loud, high notes mask the noise so boost is not necessary.

Two results of research and development undertaken by Philips—the Motional Feedback loudspeaker enclosure 22RH532/00, and the 4-channel integrated tuner/pre-amplifier/player 22RH832. (Available 1974)

The loudspeaker, outwardly conventional, is in fact very different. The name "Motional Feedback" describes its principle of operation. Expressed very simply, the movement of the cone is utilised to generate an electrical signal which is then compared electronically with the signal that actually drives it. Any differences between the intended movement (the driving signal) and the actual movement (the signal produced by the cone's vibrations) is then automatically corrected. Each loudspeaker box also contains its own power amplifiers. Just as 2-channel stereo requires two separate main amplifiers, so 4-channel needs four amplifiers. By removing these components from their conventional position within the tuner/amplifier and housing each in its respective loudspeaker cabinet, the main appliance can be more attractively styled.

The Philips' model 22RH832 is a 4-channel tuner-pre-amplifier intended for use in conjunction with these loudspeakers. An SQ decoding matrix is built in and there are facilities for connecting a CD-4 demodulator if required and for synthesizing quadraphonic sound from any existing 2-channel programme source.

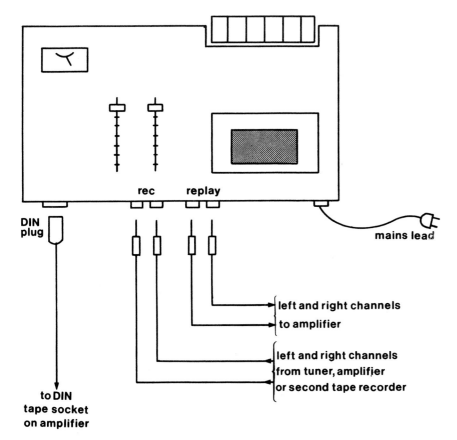

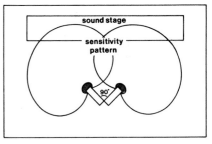

Fig. 13: Connecting a cassette recorder into the Unit Audio System.

level control and reset to this point each time. Making a cassette from a record is not so easy—and also infringes copyrights unless permission has been obtained! The recording level of most pop and popular music records is fairly constant within one LP disc so it is a simple matter to play a section into the recorder with the pause control operated to establish the correct level, and then to go back and make the recording. With classical music it is always necessary to set recording levels on the section of the LP which is loudest, since in the quieter passages the needle of the VU meter may hardly move off its end stop.

Cross fading from music to microphone may not be possible on open reel or cassette recorders with a switch to select the input. For example all sources, such as a microphone, amplifier or even another recorder may be connected to the machine but signals will not be recorded until the input selector switch, if it exists, has been correctly positioned.

Microphone recording requires a bit of practice: The ideal position is a fixed one since it helps to reduce

extraneous noise caused by handling the microphone case. For speech, the best distance from mouth to microphone is 12 to 20 inches and it should be screened from wind if outdoors.

If stereo recordings are being made, two microphones will be necessary and, of course, a stereo recorder. The microphones are usually coupled together and angled at about 90° to each other as shown in Fig. 14. Continuous experiment is needed for the best results which, in almost all cases, will depend on the location of the microphones.

Remember that sounds we do not normally take notice of—like a distant aeroplane, or a passing car or even the rustle of clothing are easily picked up and could spoil the end result.

Finally, you cannot hope to record from a loudspeaker, using a microphone, and get as good results as a direct connection to the amplifier. Special leads and adaptors are made for this purpose and should be used wherever possible.

The uses to which a cassette recorder can be put are almost as varied as the human imagination allows. For example, a personal album

Fig. 14: A plan view of two microphones arranged as a stereo pair. The angle between them is about 90°.

of events such as weddings, parties, a day at the seaside, a trip to the funfair and so on all form natural subjects for the cassette recorder.

Games such as "guess the sound" can be played where, for example, the sound of water gurgling down the sink can be made quite horrific simply by using the microphone very close to the plug-hole!

It should be remembered that not only is the cassette recorder a source of musical entertainment but also a basis for a creative hobby. Cassettes are so simply packed and posted that tape letters become simplicity itself. Finally, the recorder is so easy to operate that it can be used by all the family. ●

"One careless playing can damage a record irretrievably!"

William Arthur Chislett, O.B.E., M.A., was born in Rotherham in 1895. He first contributed to THE GRAMOPHONE in February 1925 and is now its oldest serving staff contributor. He is currently Senior Music Critic of the OXFORD MAIL, and for many years has contributed record reviews for a number of newspapers and journals. He has written a large number of record sleeve and other programme notes, and was awarded the honorary degree of Master of Arts by Oxford University in 1965 for his services to music in Oxford.

Records leave the factory in clean condition and packed in both protective inner sleeves and stout cardboard covers, but they are not always in this pristine state when sold over the counter. The ideal is always to buy records in factory-fresh condition but not many dealers can afford to keep copies for demonstration and sell only those that have not been played.

Many shops will not let customers handle records themselves, allowing only trained assistants to put them on for demonstration. *These* are the shops from which *I* would always buy. One careless playing can damage a record irretrievably.

When long-playing records were introduced 20 and more years ago, the manufacturers proclaimed their indestructability. This was a mistake, I think. It is perfectly true that unlike the old 78 records, they are difficult indeed to break. The material of which 78's were made was not only coarser but harder and more brittle, and in those days a dropped record usually meant a broken record.

It takes much more than dropping to break an LP but to set against this is the comparative softness of the material of which it is made and the supreme ease with which it can be scratched and damaged in other ways.

The biggest enemy of the LP is dust, so when not in actual use it should always be kept in the two covers designed for its well being. Unfortunately, the material of which

9 Records and tapes: purchase and care

by Bill Chislett

LP's are made holds, and persists in holding, a high charge of what is usually called static. This is of no importance so far as playing the record is concerned but it has the property of attracting and holding dust in much the same way that a magnet attracts and holds iron filings.

In the early days of LP's, I had a vivid example of the pulling power of static. I had a cat which spent much of its time on my shoulder when I was working. As I bent over the turntable to put on a record, the cat scratched itself. A loose hair started to float down gently for a moment but then suddenly straightened itself and went like an arrow direct for the record!

A dusty record quickly becomes a damaged record. Much dust is abrasive and gets ground into the record surface. The friction between stylus and record surface can generate enough heat momentarily to weld the specks of dust permanently into the record grooves, especially if the pick-up be over-heavy. But pick-up weights is another matter and is best explained in the chapter on that subject.

The elimination of static has been the subject of much research, but a suitable material for records, permanently free from static, has not yet been discovered. Most records contain static charges when new and these are likely to increase with use unless countermeasures are taken.

There are a number of proprietory products on the market designed to reduce static, but some record manufacturers recommend no more than periodic light wiping in circular motion with a soft and slightly damp cloth. I, personally, have frequently found that after treatment with a recognised dust remover, nothing else is necessary for a long time other than regular use of a groove cleaner—plus ensuring that after playing, records are returned promptly to their inner and outer sleeves.

Mishandling easily causes trouble, which is why at the outset I recommended buying only at shops which do not allow their stocks to be handled by all and sundry. Records should be handled only by their groove-free edges and the centre labels. A finger print on the record means some deposit of grease which will retain dust beyond the powers of any cleaning devices. For long years I have also kept handy a small camel hair paint brush with which to remove gently any fluff or other debris which, from time to time, however careful one is, accumulates on the stylus point.

This leads me to another frequent source of unnecessary wear—the careless placing of the stylus on the record. It should be put gently on to the rim of the record so that the widely-spaced blank run-in grooves will con-

vey it to the closer-spaced grooves which carry the programme. But there may be times when one wants to play only a piece or movement which does not start at the beginning of a record. The blank dividing bands are narrow (most of us, wanting as much music as possible for our money, would grumble it they were not) and not all hands are perfectly steady. Some pick-up arms are fitted with a device that will lower the stylus gently wherever desired, and where these are not built-in, a separate lowering device can be added quite cheaply.

Poor pick-up design, tracking errors and unsuitable styli are all prolific causes of unnecessary wear of records but these are matters for those chapters dealing with equipment. The first two are to be taken into account when buying the playing equipment but a stylus can be changed, and indeed needs to be changed periodically.

All I would say here is that however good the design of the pick-up and its arm may be, if it is fitted with a

sapphire stylus it sometimes makes sense to have this removed at the outset and replaced by a diamond stylus. Both diamonds and sapphires were described as 'permanent' in earlier days, but neither of them is. The diamond, however, is much longer lasting, and its longer playing time makes it a good investment even without taking into account the potential risk of damaging a record by a worn stylus.

Now for record storage. The rules are few and simple, but important. As is often the case, it is perhaps best to start by saying what should not be done. LP's should not be stacked in piles, one above another. The material of which they are made is quite soft and it does not take much weight or pressure partially to flatten the groove edges, and this can affect the sound substantially.

The best method of storage is to keep the records in their containers on their edges, bookwise, on shelves, placing them close enough together for each to exert a reasonable degree of side pressure on its neighbours to prevent warpage but not enough to make withdrawal difficult. Many admirable cabinets are made for the purpose, but plain bookshelves will do splendidly. An ideal arrangement is included in the Pye Model 1560 which not only provides a compact unit audio product, but also a built-in record storage cabinet which will take approximately one hundred and fifty records. The essential thing is to have uprights at reasonable intervals and that these should be smooth surfaced and at right angles.

Inevitably there will always be a section that is not completely filled and something to maintain the desirable side pressure will be needed. A large book or two will fill the space between the records and the next upright.

The only other thing to beware of is undue heat. Normal room temperature is ideal but do not place your

shelves or cabinet over or immediately beside a radiator or in front of the chimney breast.

Arrangements on shelves depend upon the size and type of individual collections. For small collections it is generally enough to arrange by types of music—orchestra, opera, and so on —as the spines of the sleeves give essential details. But for large libraries, the only real answer is to number each record, regardless of type, and keep either a loose-leaf or card index.

Now for cassettes and cartridges. The rules are much the same and really boil down to no more than common sense. Again, dust is one of the chief enemies. It can be just as abrasive to tapes as it is to LP's. So, always keep cassettes in their plastic boxes and after use put cartridges back in their sleeves or replace the plastic clip-on shields which protect the exposed tape, as the case may be.

For storing tapes at home, nothing could be better than ordinary book-shelves, but, as with LP's, beware any heat much above normal room temperature.

For storage in cars, it is a very good investment to buy one of the numerous carrying cases made to hold a number of cassettes or cartridges, and to keep it in a cool place in the car. Above all else, do not put tapes, in whatever form, on the shelf behind the rear seats where the sun can stream in and in time ruin them. Even the glove compartment can be too warm, especially if it is enclosed.

One more word about playing tapes outside the home. There are few things more calculated to damage them and their playing equipment than sand and salt, so if you must take a tape player on to the beach, you have been warned.

A less obvious hazard is the risk of accidental erasure from magnetic fields. The most likely risk in the average household is that created by the magnet of a loudspeaker. However convenient it may be to put a cassette or cartridge on top of such a speaker for a moment—DON'T. It will not damage the tape as such but may well cause partial erasure of its contents or induce increased back-

ground hiss, as also may putting the telephone on top of the tape.

Finally, if after a time the quality of sound falls below the standard you expect, do not be too ready to blame the tape, or the equipment for that matter. A certain amount of the recording material with which tapes are coated inevitably rubs off in use and any accumulation of this on the tape heads impairs the quality of the sound and a substantial accumulation can cause actual damage.

I would advise all owners of cassette or cartridge players to acquire a cleaning tape and use it regularly. Cleaning tapes consist of a length of suitably impregnated ribbon made up in cassette or cartridge form. This can be run through the player just like a recorded tape but instead of producing sound it cleans the heads of the deposit. Occasionally, but only occasionally, more elaborate cleaning may be required. Kits for this purpose can be bought but when using them take care to follow the instructions strictly, and use only the fluid provided. ●

"Quadraphonic ... Ugly as the word might be, it need frighten no-one."

In the late 1950's **Denys Killick** was consulted by the then London County Council with a view to setting up Further Education classes dealing with the subject of Tape Recording Techniques. As a result he was for many years lecturing in Evening Institutes on this subject. As Editor of TAPE RECORDING MAGAZINE (now SOUND & PIC-TURE TAPE RECORDING) Denys Killick was in close touch with all the developments in this field. He relinquished this post in order to devote more time to his own trade magazine, HI-FI TRADE JOURNAL, which he both publishes and edits. In addition to that responsibility he has also been appointed Audio Editor to CASSETTES AND CARTRIDGES, a new sister publication to THE GRAMOPHONE.

In the autumn of 1972 Denys Killick was one of three United Kingdom delegates to the CD-4 Symposium held in Japan under the auspices of Matsushita Electric Co. Ltd. of Japan.

Throughout this book there are many references to "stereo" and "stereophonic reproduction". By common usage the term has come to be regarded as synonymous with a domestic audio system using two amplified channels. Many believe the word actually means "two-channel", but this is not so. Stereo means "solid", and when applied to sound reproduction should be taken to include any system which recreates for the listener an impression of depth or solidity.

In single channel or monophonic reproduction, there is no illusion of solidity at all. With the sound coming from a single loudspeaker enclosure, we have what is known as a "point source of sound". This lacks depth and is far removed from the actual sound produced by instrumentalists at the time they performed.

Development of two-channel stereo was an enormous step forward. For reasons too technical to discuss here, the effect of reproducing specially-made stereophonic recordings over two separate amplified channels, terminating in a pair of loudspeakers enclosures, is to provide an impression of breadth.

The space between the two loudspeakers is called a "sound stage", and in a properly-balanced arrangement the listener will receive directional information from any point on a line between the loudspeakers. As a consequence, the illusion of reality of performance is greatly enhanced. Unfortunately, such a system fails in one respect—it provides breadth but not depth.

Ever since sound was first recorded and then artificially reproduced there has been unceasing effort to improve the technical quality of both recording and reproducing systems to bring them ever closer to reality. The art of audio has now reached such a degree of perfection that there can be no further dramatic improvements. As a result, the industry has been looking at two very diverse aspects of the problem. The first is to design and make reproducing equipment of smaller size, more convenient operation and lower cost, without losing too much in quality; the second is to explore one area previously neglected — to provide a genuine illusion of depth to the existing illusion of breadth so that, for example, when listening to the reproduced sound of a church organ one gets the impression not of listening to a record in a sub-urban livingroom but of actually being in church at the time of the performance.

One way to achieve this end is to use four-channel

10 Four-channel sound
by Denys Killick

(instead of two-channel) recording and reproducing systems. This is what has now become popularly known as quadraphonic sound. Ugly as the word may be, it need frighten no-one.

At the start of this chapter it was explained that stereo means "solid"—and quadraphonic reproduction is nothing more than a variation of what we might call the stereophonic theme well-known to everyone.

No, it is not the word that needs to frighten. Any cause for apprehension lies in the different ways in which the end result can be achieved, and in the additional cost and space required for such an installation.

Before discussing ways of achieving quadraphonic effects, it is reasonable to ask the fundamental question: is four-channel sound reproduction really desirable at any price?

The answer to that must be a personal opinion. At the time of writing there is no absolute agreement amongst the "experts", but the writer has studied various aspects of the problems involved, both in the United Kingdom and in Japan, and has no hesitation in affirming his own opinion that four-channel sound reproduction is not only very worth-while but offers a completely new listening experience that can be dramatically impressive.

It is fair to say that there is as much difference between four-channel and two-channel as there is between mono and two-channel.

Many readers will have had the experience of playing their older monophonic gramophone records on a stereo installation when (provided the equipment has been correctly set up) the sound will be heard coming from the two loudspeakers. The result, although a great improvement on hearing the same record played back over a single loudspeaker, is not strictly speaking "stereo" as we understand the word. In order to convey the essential directional information that gives a true impression of breadth, it is

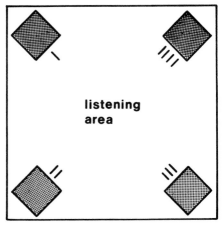

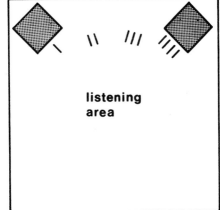

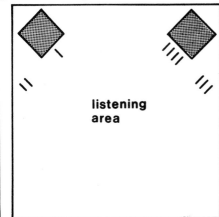

Fig. 1: This shows the theoretically ideal separation between the four channels of a domestic quadraphonic installation. There should be no cross-talk between channels and the listener should be equidistant from each loudspeaker. CD-4 is the system to approach this ideal most closely. In practice, it is often advantageous to position the rear channel loudspeaker enclosures at the sides instead of at the rear, or alternatively the listening area can be shifted from the centre to the rear wall.

Fig. 2: When a record that has been recorded via an SQ encoding matrix is reproduced on an ordinary 2-channel stereo system the information that would have been passed to the rear channels does not disappear; it can still be heard but it will have been "folded in" to a position between the two loudspeakers.

Fig. 3: Similarly when a record that has been recorded via a QS matrix is reproduced on an ordinary 2-channel system the rear channel information is again retained, but this time it will seem to come from an area outside the sound stage formed by the two loudspeaker enclosures.

necessary for the recording to have been deliberately made initially as a two-channel disc.

The same reasoning extends into four-channel. It is possible to take an ordinary two-channel sound source, such as a stereophonic broadcast or gramophone record, and to reproduce it via two separate two-channel (stereophonic) amplifiers, each driving a pair of loudspeakers with one pair in the normal frontal position and the other pair on the sides or at the back of the listening room. The result of such an arrangement will be four-channel of a kind, but it will be far removed from real quadraphonic reproduction.

There are, however, other ways of achieving four-channel effects from two-channel sources. One of these involves what are commonly described as "synthesizers". In the early days of two-channel stereo, many manufacturers marketed so-called "synthesizers" that were claimed to enhance the stereophonic effects from monophonic gramophone records. These had varying degrees of success.

With the passage of time there have been vast improvements in electronic techniques and as a consequence some four-channel synthesizing circuits can give very pleasant listening experiences. The actual form of the equipment required varies according to the manufacturer of the product. Some of the latest two-channel stereo amplifiers also include four-channel synthesizing facilities so that the user has only to add a second stereo amplifier, together with a second pair of loudspeakers, to enjoy this form of four-channel reproduction.

In other cases, the synthesizer plus the necessary additional amplifier equipment is all built into a single unit such as the Pye Stereo Plus 2 convertor which has been designed as a "package deal" to enable the user of existing stereophonic equipment to convert simply and easily to four-channel reproduction.

Another term sometimes used to describe this kind of sound reproduction is "ambiophony". This is derived from the word "ambient" which is defined in the Oxford dictionary as meaning "surrounding". The reason why two-channel stereophonic reproduction does not convey an impression of solidity is because it is not capable of accurately reproducing the ambience of the concert hall.

When listening to a live performance, the audience receives aural information directly from the instrumentalists but to this is added a great deal of sound that is reflected back from the walls and the ceiling. It is the amount of this reflected sound that conveys to the listener the sense of the spaciousness, and indeed the character, of the auditorium. Every room, hall or church where music is performed has its own individual acoustic character. The sound of a big organ being played in a small church could never be confused with the sound of the same instrument as heard in a great cathedral.

The enormous acoustic differences that occur even within one's own home can be investigated very easily. Clap your hands in the living room and try to remember the character of the sound. Do the same thing in a tiled bathroom or kitchen and the difference will be immediately obvious. The origin of the sound was identical in both cases; it is the ambience that has changed.

In synthesized four-channel sound reproduction, or in ambiophony, parts of the frontal two-channel stereo sound are extracted and fed via a separate amplifier to another pair of loudspeaker enclosures situated at other points in the listening room. The aim is to simulate the kind of reflections that might have been heard during the live performance. But because these rear channel sounds are extracts from the front channels and not true reflections they can never be quite right.

So it must be said that none of these systems offers true four-channel because they all rely on modifying two-channel sources to produce four-channel effects. Nevertheless, they do offer the most inexpensive means of bringing quadraphonic reproduction into the largest number of homes. Many will not want to investigate further. They will find that the sound produced by synthesizing devices offers complete satisfaction.

But for those inclined to pursue the matter further, there now arises a series of unhappy complications. Troubles arise because there is more than one way of deriving four-channels of recorded information from the single groove of a gramophone record, and these different methods are not absolutely compatible.

'Discrete' system

Different manufacturers have developed different systems and at the time of writing we have a situation where a number of record producing companies are manufacturing discs to different specifications.

The ideal four-channel record/playback system would be one in which each channel is recorded and played back quite independently of the other three. Such a system is called "discrete", meaning "separate". All forms of magnetic tape recording are, by their very nature, discrete, and so we find the emergence of four-channel quadraphonic open spool tape recorders, four-channel eight-track cartridges and playback machines. None of these presents problems of compatibility because of the inherent separateness of the recording and playback channels.

But as soon as we try to record the same four channels within the confines of the single groove of a gramophone record, we are in trouble. The enormity of the technical problem should be self-evident.

One way of overcoming it is to follow the method invented by J.V.C. Nivico of Japan, called CD-4. The letter C stands for "compatible", the letter D for "discrete" and the figure 4 for four-channel. Without going into

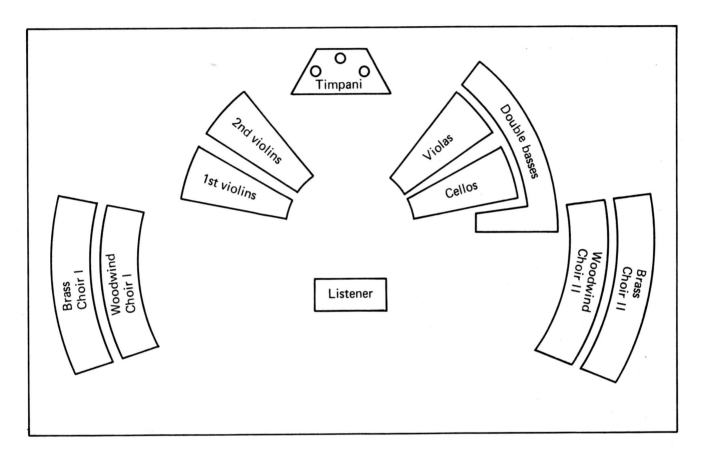

Fig. 4: When RCA recorded The Philadelphia Orchestra under Eugene Ormandy performing Bach's Greatest Fugues *in CD-4 (ARDI-0026) the orchestral forces were deliberately arranged to give the spatial effect shown in this diagram on playback. If the record is reproduced on a 2-channel stereo system all the left-hand information, both front and rear, will be fed to the left-hand loudspeaker and front and rear right will go to the right-hand one.*

technical details of the method it is sufficient to say that such a disc has a degree of separateness or discreteness in its four channels that cannot be achieved by any other disc-recording system.

Its disadvantages lie in the fact that such a record must be played using a special cartridge/stylus combination (preferably using what is known as the Shibata profile stylus) and the signal has to be fed to a special "demodulator" whose function is to sort out the four channels. From thence the output of the demodulator is fed to two two-channel ampliers (or a single four-channel one), and when connections are made to four loudspeaker enclosures, we have true quadraphonic reproduction.

In its initial stages the system suffered from reduced programme time on gramophone records and the need to cut the masters more slowly than is normal practice in the industry. The inventors claim that these disadvantages have either been overcome or are about to be. On the credit side, we have what is claimed to be "true compatibility" with all existing monophonic and stereophonic

domestic equipment so that a CD-4 disc will reproduce correctly either as mono, as stereo or as four-channel, solely dependent upon the kind of equipment used to play it back.

The CD-4 system is unique to J.V.C. Nivico and their associated company, National Panasonic. Other manufacturers have adopted a totally different approach to this very difficult problem. All other true four-channel systems use a device known as a "matrix".

Again avoiding technicalities, it will be sufficient to explain that the four separate channels are "encoded" during the record process and then "decoded" in the user's home through the action of a decoding matrix in the playback amplifier.

This would be fine if the different kinds of matrix all followed identical lines. Unfortunately they do not.

Whatever system is being considered, it is quite useless unless an adequate supply of discs recorded to that specification is in fact available.

By now the reader will have appreciated something of

the complexities of quadraphonic sound reproduction. This is why we asked the original question: is it worth it?

Despite all the problems it is sincerely believed that it is. The intending purchaser has to face the additional cost of two extra amplified channels together with loudspeakers, the cost of the matrix and/or demodulator, plus, in the case of CD-4, the special cartridge. He or she has to decide which of the systems to use and has to decide also whether or not to concentrate solely on tape in the form of eight-track cartridges as a reproducing medium (in which case he is likely to suffer from a very restricted repertoire) or to invest in the full-scale disc equipment.

Most of the true quadraphonic systems also incorporate synthesizing facilities. This means that whenever using conventional two-channel sound sources (such as stereo broadcasts, gramophone records or tapes) it is possible at the turn of a knob to enjoy this material in what has been called a "pseudo four-channel" form. This is roughly equivalent to the lower cost synthesizers mentioned earlier in this chapter, and it does mean that the user is not going to be restricted to the special four-channel records now beginning to be produced.

Looking back to the early days of two-channel stereo it will be recalled that the vast majority of gramophone records were then manufactured and sold as monophonic discs and stereo equivalents were a comparative rarity. Gradually, they became more common until a few years ago most record companies abandoned the manufacture of mono discs and nowadays virtually all recorded repertoire is available only in stereo format.

By the use of a stereo compatible cartridge, such discs can successfully be reproduced as mono by the owners of mono equipment.

One of the over-riding requirements for all four-channel record systems is that they should be compatible with mono and stereo players. As a result it is not unreasonable to look forward to the day when all gramophone records will be four-channel and the two-channel stereo record as we know it today will be a thing of the past. The importance of this change will be its achievement without rendering any existing equipment obsolete. Of course it is not going to happen next month or next year, but there is a strong possibility that such a situation will arise at some time in the future. When it does it need worry no-one, any more than the change from mono to stereo gave rise for concern.

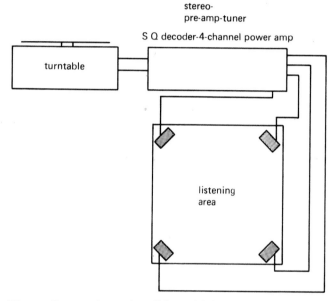

Fig. 5: Integrated tuner/amplifiers with built-in decoders permit simple, uncomplicated installation, requiring only two more loudspeakers and their leads as compared to 2-channel stereo.

No discussion of four-channel sound reproduction would be complete without making some reference to the controversy that now exists about the ways in which four-channel records should be recorded. It was explained earlier that the purpose of a four-channel system is to convey an impression of solidity by reproducing the ambience of the concert hall through an additional pair of amplified channels and loudspeaker enclosures. As soon as the technical means of accomplishing this end became a practical possibility, musicians and record producers began to extend the line of their thought into other directions.

"Why", they ask, "is a symphony orchestra placed on a stage in a large hall with the audience facing them?"

The reason, of course, is to provide the physical accommodation for both the musicians and the audience. No such limitation occurs within the home where the musicians are not "live" and the audience is tiny. Thinking back into the history of music and musical performance it was at once realised that the trend towards large orchestras in large concert halls is a relatively modern development.

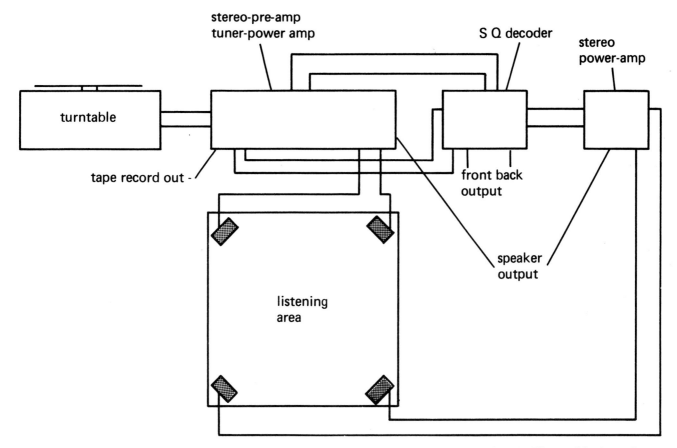

Fig. 6: Connections are a little more complicated when adapting an existing 2-channel system to 4-channel. The amplifier has to have an "after record monitor" facility and this is wired to the decoder. A separate 2-channel amplifier is then required to drive the rear loud-speakers, although this is sometimes integrated within the decoder itself. The diagram shows them as separate components.

When the appreciation of music was the prerogative of wealthy princelings and patrons there was a much more intimate contact between players and listeners.

Through the use of modern technology it is now possible to return to that intimacy in the form of quadraphonic sound reproduction, the chief difference lying in the fact that it can now be enjoyed by the majority instead of the few. Consequently we have two main streams of thought in the four-channel recording of classical music: one insists on devoting every effort towards recreating the actual ambience of the concert hall within the listener's home whilst the other is devoted to the exploration of completely new musical experiences by redistributing the musicians in relation to the listener and bringing both into closer contact.

So far as pop music is concerned, this has never relied upon the true representation of sounds actually heard in a recording studio and so it at once lends itself to the further extension of creative effects which can now be distributed in space around the listener through the use of four channels.

All these developments are of the greatest interest and it is probable that in the years to come they will be responsible for generating compositions and performances that will be very different in character to any of the music we are familiar with today.

Perhaps this chapter should close with an apology for the confusion it might have engendered in the reader's mind. But at the time of writing the entire industry is confused about four-channel and its complexities. Were the writer called upon to advocate one system in preference to the others he would be hard put to it to find an adequate answer.

He is certain only about one thing: four-channel sound reproduction is a new and exciting experience that can be thoroughly enjoyed by those who take the time and the trouble to find their way through the labyrinth of confusion that surrounds it. ●

An audio unit at well below £100.

Keen shoppers are always interested in the value they get for their money: that remains true whether everyday items or bigger household possessions are to be bought. But the cheapest buy does not necessarily represent the best value—and nowhere is this more true than in unit audio and hi-fi.

It is also true that fair value is to be found at several price levels. Choice depends on individual needs and, especially, on the listener's personal ambitions in respect of stereo realism and the subtleties of sound quality. And there is also an outstanding factor that weighs more heavily than most—the surroundings in which the audio system is to be used.

A really big lounge deserves a big system, and it is virtually impossible to create a realistic effect unless there is enough reserve power. The smaller system, which would sound lost and inadequate in such spacious quarters, will be much more at home in the comparatively restricted surroundings of a town flat.

Planning starts with a budget. This may be enough for unit audio of less than hi-fi quality, up to about £100, or in the medium range, up to £250 or so. Or it may be in the luxury high-power category, ranging up to £500 and beyond. Even if the purchaser has firm ideas about how much to spend to meet his particular conditions of use (size of room, etc) it is still advisable to know how to apportion the budget effectively.

Assuming separate units for record playing, the division at the £100 level is about: 25% for the player, including cartridge, 45% for the pair of loudspeakers and 30% for the amplifier. For such an outlay, think in terms of an amplifier rated at around 8 to 10 watts per channel, a pair of bookshelf speakers and a simple turntable/arm unit, fitted with a magnetic cartridge and complete with a base and dust cover.

At the level of £150 and above it is possible that the three main parts of the system would each claim about a third of the total—a little more for the speakers if necessary. In this area, too, it is possible to plan for one of the transcription turntable units mentioned earlier, and the variety of high quality pickup cartridges is particularly wide. So it will repay the new enthusiast to give special thought to the components at each end of the system. Careful listening is a good aid to the decision.

Sources of programmes other than recordings have to be considered. This may not be practicable for low-budget audio but great strides have been made to produce excellent low-priced equipment. However, it becomes more important if outlay is higher. Obviously the budget must be adjusted if VHF/FM radio is to feature initially in the system; and the same is true if a cassette unit is to be included.

Fortunately, audio systems are versatile and permit the addition of such items at a later date. For instance, there is rarely any problem in adding a radio tuner, and generally the same is true of cassette machines, many of which are in record/replay unit form and therefore ideally designed for linking to a unit system. Larger spool-to-spool tape recorders can also be connected.

> *"Getting value for money means planning a budget."*

Most unit systems are accommodated on shelves or wall furniture, and because of this free-standing layout any extension of the equipment is unlikely to be troublesome. We can say the same of quadraphonic layouts, for the additions that occupy space are the extra speakers.

However, there is an obvious trend toward 'combination' systems in which all parts except the loudspeakers are housed in one cabinet—an arrangement that makes for compactness and offers new scope to designers. The strongest appeal is to customers who favour plug-in-and-play equipment and simplified planning. Earlier remarks about room size apply to these systems, which are mostly in the popular medium-cost range.

Some simple examples of these compact outfits are available at around £60 and there are many more at £100 or more. Clearly there is a mounting demand, and manufacturers are responding with new and attractive models. Many record-buyers do not aspire to genuine hi-fi, and the well designed combination system can give them what they require in a space-saving and convenient format. Especially suitable for the smaller room (with a few exceptions among the higher-powered models), such outfits eliminate the interconnections inevitable in a unit system yet can incorporate record-playing, cassettes and radio—one or all of these. Without doubt we shall see more plug-in-and-play audio of this kind.

As anyone who scans the advertisements can observe, some audio is very expensive. It is possible to assemble a no-compromise system costing £500 or even more. Although inexperienced listeners are not always prepared to believe it, this kind of expenditure can secure good value. With acquired expertise or borrowed

11
Value for money
by Clement Brown

See page 24 for author biographical notes.

professional help, the fortunate enthusiast with this sort of budget can concentrate on quality and refinement. Of course, the much-discussed law of diminishing returns eventually has an effect, and we reach the stage where a little extra costs a great deal more.

As an example, among some very fine loudspeakers at present on the market there are two models that might well feature in high-powered installations of the most advanced type. One model sells at nearly £100 (per speaker) and the other at more than £150. One is a bit bulkier than the other but the performance differences are sublte rather than dramatic, being mainly concerned with the deep

bass and the characteristic quality of the middle of the frequency range.

So the discerning buyer must listen carefully and consider the implications. If he decides, after soul searching, that the subtleties lead him back to the bigger model, he is faced with more than £100 extra for the stereo system!

Again, one pickup cartridge at £30 is very good: another sells at £60 and is a *little* better to those who provide conditions of use that will permit the subtle difference to be enjoyed. In fact the more expensive model will quite likely attract the listener who is won over by the musical superiority of the more costly loudspeaker. If he has ears for these small but significant

improvements, he will never again be satisfied with an inferior standard. And who is to say he is not getting good value for money?

Reverting to more basic matters, there are prospects of improving smaller systems—but it depends on the reason for change or modification. Generally, audio systems can be upgraded provided they are in unit form. Any component of the system can be replaced — a better turntable, a more powerful amplifier to meet new demands — so long as the user checks that basic matching is not in doubt.

Relatively small changes may not cost much, although it will be agreed that they are not worth pursuing unless there is a demonstrable improvement — one that can be heard. For example, some listeners may find that changed circumstances make it worth while to trade-in speakers for better models. More relevant to most requirements in popular-priced systems, however, is an eventual upgrading of the record-playing unit.

Substitution of a better cartridge is an obvious possibility, but the suitability of the pickup arm has to be checked. The same care is needed in the event of replacement of the stylus by another having improved characteristics. It is a good line to investigate, though, because stylus renewal effectively renews the cartridge.

To many readers thinking of buying their first Unit Audio or those who are not real hi-fi addicts, the complexities of separate units with all the extra wiring may be too much. The Combination Unit Audio System is the answer.

First think in terms of what use you will put the equipment to and compare with what you are prepared to pay. ●

Combination unit audio may be the answer.

"Performance, appearance, durability, and safety—that's the key to manufacturing success!"

Stanley Benson is a freelance journalist who has written about industrial subjects for a wide variety of UK and overseas publications. He edits and produces industrial and business publications and is particularly interested in how human factors influence both the quantity and quality of production.

Audio manufacturers seek above all for *quality* in their products: quality of performance, quality of appearance, durability and, of course, safety. There is a constant search to improve all these attributes and success is ensured only by making sure that quality is born during design and construction; it cannot be put in afterwards. This is why quality control marches side by side with every stage, from initial design, through manufacture, to final packing and despatch.

Different firms have slightly varying systems but this chapter describes broadly the manufacture and quality control of any piece of audio equipment.

Let us assume an up-dated model of a piece of equipment is about to be launched on the market. Since there are new elements in the unit, some components or parts will have to be specially designed and made, but a large proportion of the 'bits and pieces' will be bought, ready-made, from components manufacturers and are more or less standard. Not always, though; makers of components

One of the assembly lines at the Pye audio factory at Stevenage, Herts.

12 Manufacturing the audio product

by Stanley Benson

The most stringent tests ensure maximum quality in today's audio equipment.

are also ever-striving to improve their products. Thus, from the very beginning, the quality control engineers come into the picture. They will have been consulted at design stage, along with servicing specialists, who will advise how easily or otherwise a particular design can be repaired or serviced when necessary.

As the components that have been ordered come to the factory, they are rigorously inspected to ensure that they conform to the specifications of the original design. Meanwhile, the new 'bits'—an electronic part possibly, or maybe a cabinet—are being produced. Anything between 15 and 25 complete 'sets' will now be made . . . *by hand.* There are no jigs, no special manufacturing equipment, yet in existence for mass production. Metal is cut out by hand, wood is carved; these are the 'guinea pigs' for the model-to-be.

About ten of these unique, hand-made units are now put out for 'long life' tests—checking their resistance to high and low temperatures, exposure to voltage surges,

even such factors as their ability to stand up to strong sunlight without discolouring. Car radios will be fitted into engineers' own cars and tested for months under actual driving conditions, bumps, jerks and all.

Other units will be tested on the bench in countless ways. For example, a toggle-switch on a set will be automatically joggled up and down maybe ten thousand times, until it has been worked to destruction; the glue, the paints, the varnishes, the timbers or plastics to be used, will all be subjected to rigorous testing.

So much for the unit . . . so far. If found acceptable, it will have to be manufactured and tested again and again. Since there are new elements in our example, special equipment will have to be built—say, a new press to stamp out the chassis. This new equipment must be tested to ensure that it will work smoothly throughout the production run. Even test equipment may have to be specially designed and constructed.

Assuming that quality control has accepted the 'guinea

Assembling radiograms, loudspeakers and other audio equipment into their cabinets at Pye's Stevenage factory.

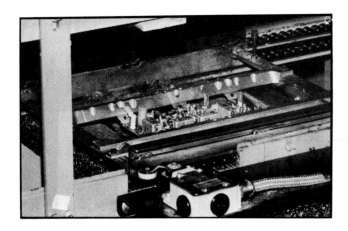

During manufacture circuit boards are passed over a solder bath in which temperature levels are maintained very accurately.

Quality control staff virtually pull to pieces the first prototypes of a new model for tests.

pig' models, work starts on the 'pre-production run' of perhaps 100 prototypes. This pre-production run is designed as much to check the manufacturing processes as the unit itself. To take only one example: the engineers maintain a check on the temperature of the solder used in preparing circuit boards, to make certain it will stay constant hour after hour, because an error here could seriously damage the boards. The engineers will have already checked the accessibility of various components that will have to be reached by a service engineer if later

on something goes amiss . . . there is no use having an advanced component if it cannot be got at when necessary.

Quality control more of less pulls these hundred prototype sets to pieces again, examining whether the bolts fit properly into the nuts, that screws are correctly home and, of course, testing the performance, the output, distortion levels and sensitivity.

While this goes on test equipment maintains constant checks on such points as the current and voltages that will flow through the printed circuit boards; a faulty board is

On the drawing board the search goes on for better and better audio products.

automatically rejected. In most firms there are also at least twice-daily random checks on components as they come off the production line, even before final assembly.

The production batch of models is finished. Now comes a 'customer check', by specially-trained girls who approach each unit as if they were buying it themselves. Here the senses of hearing, sight and touch come into play, re-checking so much that has already been tested by machinery.

Now each unit has to be packed. Very often the package itself will have been specially designed to accommodate a new shape or a weight, and the quality control men check the packaging as thoroughly as the equipment, even including a ruthless 'drop test' . . . which speaks for itself! They also make sure that the instruction booklet is enclosed!

Even when a newly-manufactured batch of sets is packed and is standing in a storeroom ready for despatch, quality control engineers will take out random samples, unpack them and check them once more. Before the 100 units are given 'sales clearance' a special listeners panel is set up for detailed listening appraisal of the sound quality and acceptability in the home.

The care that is taken involves thousands of man-hours and it is fair to say that the amount of time spent on testing and quality control about equals that of the actual manufacture of a piece of audio equipment.

Companies importing equipment from abroad in general take great care to ensure that the quality of such products equals that of equipment manufactured in their own factories. Bearing in mind that a proper quality control check of a typical unit will take an hour, an

Quality control is given top priority. Products are taken at random from the assembly lines for intensive testing.

engineer can test no more than eight sets a day.

One sizeable audio factory at Stevenage, therefore uses a system based on mathematical probabilities, and it is the same as that employed for Ministry of Defence specifications for anything from a minute electronic component to a rifle. If the batch to be brought in consists, for example, of anything between 10,001 and 35,000, the quality control engineers will test 315 of them. And until they have approved the batch the whole consignment, from home or abroad, is 'frozen' so far as public distribution is concerned.

The testers employ a system which allocates points to faults listed as 'A' ,'B' and 'C'. An 'A' fault is something totally unacceptable under any circumstances, and it gets ten points or demerits. A 'B' fault is anything that is likely to be noticed and rejected—even though it does not affect performance—by a *critical* customer, and collects five points. A 'C' fault is something such as small scratches or marks which have no effect on performance but would be damaging to the firm's reputation for quality. These get one point.

This system enables the engineers to evaluate the whole batch very accurately. If general quality is found to be up to standard, they will be able to reduce the number of tests on subsequent batches of the same size and the same model to 125 units.

Suppose, however, that half a million sets are coming in from, say, the Continent or the Far East. Then no fewer than 1,250 tests will be made from each batch. And when you consider that a typical hi-fi unit can contain up to 100 condensers and 175 resistors—all of which must be tested—the size of the problem is immediately apparent. ●

Trays in front of each girl on the line contain the parts she needs for her stage in the product assembly.

*"Choosing
audio equipment
to suit your pocket
and fit your home"*

John Catchpole is a technical liaison officer at Pye, with particular responsibilities in the audio field. He has been actively engaged with audio development since he joined the company in 1948, and took a leading part in promoting stereo in its early days. He is well known in the industry as a technical lecturer and for his audio demonstrations.

The authors of the various articles in our book, each a specialist in his field, have dealt fully with the component parts of the sound reproducing system. It only remains now to consider how best one can acquire such equipment at a price within one's pocket, and, perhaps of more importance, accommodate the units without disrupting domestic furnishing and harmony.

How much?

Whilst price can form a reasonable guide as to the sound quality one may expect from equipment, technical performance above a certain standard is usually only achieved by an increase in price somewhat disproportionately greater than the improvement in performance. When considering anything less than a noncompromise system the main concern therefore should be to achieve the reproduction of music for the pleasure given by listening to it. It does not follow that an installation consisting of units designed in strict conformity to the "scientifically perfect" specification will necessarily give the most satisfying reproduction of music. Although a listener may be quite familiar with the tones of orchestral instruments, it is not impossible that if these tones are altered in a certain way, they would be considered more satisfactory.

It has been found when conducting comparative listening tests of two

13
Sound ideas for your home

by John Catchpole

different amplifier/speaker systems, that quite large groups of listeners have judged the less technically perfect system to give more "natural" and therefore more satisfactory sound.

We do not suggest from this that one should be satisfied with equipment of inferior specification, but merely that having decided on a specification within one's pocket, the final choice should be dictated by the listening test—by which you as the purchaser judge the most pleasing and satisfactory sound reproduction.

How many watts?

From Chapters 4 and 7 the reader will know that the power output of an amplifier is quoted in watts and is purely a measurement of the electrical energy available at its output terminals when measured in a specific manner.

The loudspeaker, when connected to the amplifier, converts the electrical energy into sound energy; therefore the level of sound from the loudspeaker will depend almost entirely on how efficiently the speaker performs the conversion. Also loudspeaker systems which give the widest and smoothest response are not necessarily the most efficient. Other factors which must be taken into account when deciding on amplifier power are, room size and acoustics. Try this by listening to a good portable radio first in the bathroom and then in a furnished living room.

Assuming a loudspeaker efficiency of 3-5%, John Gilbert (page 46) suggests an amplifier power rating in excess of 15 watts for a room of modest size, say 12'—14' with average ceiling height. This of course can only be taken as a guide since most of the controlling factors have been averaged, but it perhaps emphasises the advice given by the authors that a listening test in your home is the only satisfactory way of reaching a decision.

How will it fit in?

Accommodating a sound system in the home was, at one time, somewhat of a problem, mainly because the ladies tended to resist their menfolk cluttering up the lounge with all the "bits and pieces", as they called the bulky valve amplifiers and huge loudspeakers of the past. The writer well remembers the day he first introduced a 9 cubic foot speaker enclosure into the lounge; it took hours of explaining, but the sounds it made eventually won the day.

Transistor amplifiers and modern loudspeaker techniques have eased the problem to the extent perhaps that the ladies in general are now as "audio conscious" as the men. This is evidenced by the yearly increasing female attendance at various Audio Fairs and Shows.

Today manufacturers of audio equipment realise that good sound need no longer be restricted to the technically-minded enthusiast, with the result that technicians and top rate industrial designers are working together to produce equipment which not only reaches hi-fi standard but which looks well in the home. This comment from one of today's leading industrial designers currently engaged in the field makes this point:

"A hi-fi must be good to look at, but it also has to be kept clean and dusted. Thus the trend now to the 'soft' look, with edges rounded away for easier dusting. If there are valid reasons for using a material that is a natural dust-collector, an anti-static agent is incorporated to act as a dust-repellent. Thoughtful design avoids using materials that discolour and look shabby as time passes; these factors matter rather more to women than to men. On the whole, women are strongly influenced by an audio set's suitability as a piece of furniture and its ability to fit in with a room's decor. Men are more concerned with the 'works' and with the controls. Here, the familiarity with car dashboards and the illumination used in instrumentation has greatly influenced the design of audio controls.

Colour matters for controls—with black and grey now predominating—and so does touch and sound. In designing a control great attention is paid to how it feels, and to avoiding an ugly, irritating sound when it is switched on and off. Again, the car has become an influence through the familiar, satisfying, confident clunk of a car door closing.

In the arrangements of the controls, the one-time impressive powerful-looking array of identical knobs and switches is giving way to placing the most-used and the least-used in separate groups, making for easier operation. For the future it very much looks as though an Italian concept of hiding the controls away in a cockpit in the side or back of the case will gain increasing popularity. Utility matters in audio design, as it does in furniture; so do looks, craftsmanship, and quality of materials. But not all these things matter to the same degree to everybody.

The Reproduction style, for people who like an antique look (although the material will be 20th century), is increasing in popularity. The Modern style—simple, clean, neat (which is mainly Scandinavian-influenced)—remains the first choice for most British women. Others like the sophisticated, fashionable Italian look. But whatever the style, there are elements common to all good design: purpose, utility, and survival-value. Audio design is no exception".

How to acquire it

From the preceding chapters it will be obvious to the reader that there are basically two ways of going about setting up an audio system.
1. The acquisition of a series of separate units, i.e. turntable, pickup, amplifier, tuner, speaker and tape recorder, which, as series of "building bricks", can, on a DIY basis, be suitably mounted and wired together to form a complete system.
2. The purchase of a Combination Unit (plug-in-and-play system.)

Separates

This of course will involve careful planning and the necessary technical expertise or reliable advice in order to

select the right units to provide the best value within the budgeted expenditure. Separates have one great advantage since, as "building bricks", the various units can from time to time be replaced as improvement or upgrading is required. Many enthusiasts, today in possession of top grade non-compromise systems, have started off with quite modest outfits, but they have been careful enough to plan each purchase with the final system in mind.

If this is the choice then start at the "heart" with a good quality amplifier of sufficient power output and input sensitivities to meet your later requirements. You may find that this unit alone, plus a pair of reasonable speakers, will swallow up the first year budget and you may have to accept temporarily a less good pickup. But not to worry, at least you will have "got going". The advice given in this book will serve to guide you on how improvements can be achieved.

There is available on the market today a wide choice of combination Tuner-Amplifier turntable units even to the latest combination 'ensemble' providing Tuner Amplifier Turntable and Cassette Tape Recorder all housed together as one unit. Two separate loudspeaker enclosures complete the system. Our picture on page 33 shows how such a system can quite easily and neatly be accommodated in a modern wall furnishing unit. This would look just as well on a single shelf unit across a corner or alcove. With such a system the manufacturer has done all the hard work for you; there will be no need to worry about pickup, tuner, and speaker matching. You need only follow the manufacturer's unpacking and setting-up instructions and then get down to the important part of speaker positioning. This is up to you, and however unscientific it may seem, it is best arrived at by trail and error. In many rooms a corner position is best; however, remember furnishings, carpets and curtains will have considerable effect, so it is a good plan to start tests from the corner position and then follow the advice given on page 76. Have a good listening period, a whole evening of varied music if you can. Try to imagine yourself in the concert hall or at the live performance. If you find you can do this with ease and begin to feel "there" then you are approaching the right speaker position. Remember you are seeking to create a sound stage as near to the real performance as possible.

The best tests

A live FM Radio broadcast in stereo possibly provides the best signal source for such tests, but whether it is radio or disc the volume setting you choose must be adjusted with care. At too low a volume the dynamic range and illusion will be somewhat lost. If it is too great you will rapidly become fatigued, even if the neighbours don't!

It is a good plan to set the volume on a speaking voice or a single instrument such as a piano and adjust to the level you would expect to hear if the person or instrument were actually in the room.

Much has been written about speaker positioning; this is because it is one of the most important factors in obtaining good stereo. The diagrams on page 77 are a guide, but remember it may be necessary to adjust one's

listening positioning as well as that of the speakers. It should be possible to find a listening area large enough for several people to hear good stereo. It is most important when setting up to follow the manufacturer's instructions. Particular attention should first be paid to the mains voltage adjustment, correct connection of the mains lead, and use of the specified mains fuse rating.

Depending on how you purchase the equipment the supplier will in most cases carry out the installation for you; however, here for guidance are a few points to observe:

Most manufacturers protect against transit damage; so make sure that any transit screws, such as those securing the turntable assembly, are removed before switching on.

Stylus pressure and pickup arm bias compensation must be adjusted correctly according to the manufacturer's recommendation, otherwise the stylus tracing of the record groove will not be correct and distortion will occur noticeably mainly as a fuzziness on fairly loud passages and upper frequencies.

Remember that the transmission of sound vibration from the speaker to the pickup, via the shelf or surface on which the player is positioned, can cause a continuous audible oscillation known as acoustic feedback. Although most manufacturers take care to "cushion" the turntable and pickup against this with special suspension mountings, it is still possible to provoke sufficient feedback should a speaker be positioned too near the player unit. This can easily occur where wall furniture is used, but should it be necessary to mount a speaker and player on the same wall unit then the difficulty can be overcome by using some form of resilient material such as felt or foam rubber under the speaker cabinet. Alternatively it may be sufficient to move the player to another section of the wall unit which may be mechanically 'decoupled' from its adjoining section.

If the equipment is purchased as a complete system, i.e. including speakers, there should be no difficulty with the interfacing connections—plugs and sockets will match; however, take care should it be necessary to extend the loudspeaker leads. Reversal of the wires to one speaker will place it 'out of phase' with the other, resulting in loss of correct stereo effect. Pre-assembled loud-speaker extension leads are available from hi-fi dealers and are preferable to the use of connector blocks. Never attempt a "twist up and insulate" job; a short circuit at this point could easily cause serious damage to the amplifier output stages.

One final point about selection of discs. If you have already built up a library of recordings which have been played on a medium quality record player or stereogram you may be surprised to find their condition is not as good as you thought. The reason, of course, is that the extended frequency response of the hi-fi system is now letting you hear surface scratches and even severe groove damage caused by imperfect tracking of the previous pickup. When purchasing new records you will soon appreciate that hi-fi starts on the disc. In general the higher priced discs provide a fairly consistently good standard. Some budget discs are surprisingly good, others are surprisingly poor. Careful choice and study of record reviews to be found in magazines devoted to the subject will prevent disappointment.

Properly set up, your new sound system should give you and your family hours of pleasurable listening. ●

Glossary

A

ACOUSTICS: (a) The science or study of sound, its production, transmission, reception and effects.
(b) The acoustical characteristics of halls and rooms.

ACOUSTIC FEEDBACK: Unwanted acoustic interaction between output and input of an audio system, usually between loudspeaker and pick-up or microphone. May be heard as a howling or roaring noise as sound vibrations from the loudspeakers reach the pick-up.

ACOUSTICAL RESISTANCE UNIT: (ARU) A device of predetermined acoustical resistance juxtaposed with the port opening of a reflex loudspeaker. Controls Q factor, or frequency response.

ACOUSTIC SUSPENSION: Loudspeaker system employing a sealed cabinet so that the acoustic stiffness of the enclosed air provides the main restoring force for the loudspeaker cone.

AERIAL (ANTENNA): The part of a radio system that radiates or receives signals from space.

AFC (AUTOMATIC FREQUENCY CONTROL): A circuit which automatically keeps an FM receiver locked on to the desired station.

ALIGNMENT PROTRACTOR: Simple tool for judging error in alignment of pick-up arm in relation to record and turntable. Only necessary when a separate arm is used with turntable.

AM (AMPLITUDE MODULATION): Modulation accomplished by varying the instantaneous amplitude of the carrier wave. Radio broadcasts on SW, MW and LW are AM transmissions. The amplitude of the radio signal varies according to the strength of the impressed modulating signal (microphone, disc, tape).

AMBIENCE: Acoustic environment. Increasingly used to mean the degree and character of the reverberant sound accompanying recordings.

AMBIOPHONY: Derived from Ambience to describe a multiple speaker system which reproduces stereophonic sound through four or more speakers, thus generating a sound field with depth.

AM/FM RECEIVER: A radio capable of receiving both amplitude and frequency modulated transmissions.

AMPLIFIER: An electronic unit designed to increase the level of any signal presented to it, i.e. more signal from the output than delivered to the input.

AMPLITUDE: The strength of an oscillation or vibration. It can be measured in volts, amps., feet, millimetres or any other unit, depending on the nature of the oscillation or vibration.

ANECHOIC CHAMBER: A room without reverberation. This special type of room or chamber has acoustically absorbent walls, ceiling and floors. Used for audio equipment measurements.

ANTI-SKATE (FORCE): A small amount of outward side force deliberately applied to a pick-up arm to counter the centripetal force or inward swing, present when the stylus tracks the record groove.

ARMATURE: Moving part in a pick-up cartridge e.g. metal part consisting of cantilever and magnetic material pivoted to form a stylus assembly in a magnetic cartridge.

ATTENUATOR: A device used to cut down signals which are too strong to process in an amplifier or receiver.

AUDIO: A term encompassing the art of sound recording and reproduction. (Latin —I hear.)

AUDIO BANDWITH: The range of audio frequencies which an electronic system can or should reproduce. It usually implies the upper and lower frequency limit of such a system.

AUDIO FREQUENCY: A frequency at which a sound wave is normally audible (like the frequencies associated with the instruments of the orchestra). Approximately 15 Hz to 20,000 Hz for a child, but a narrower range for an adult, typically 30 to 15,000 Hz.

AUDIO SIGNAL: The electrical signal derived from sounds such as speech and music. An audio signal is usually produced from either a microphone, tape, disc or radio.

AUTOMATIC DISC STOP: An electro-mechanical or electrical device which stops the turntable rotating and may lift the tone arm from the record.

AUTOMATIC RECORDING LEVEL CONTROL: A control circuit used in tape and cassette tape recorders where no manual adjustment of recording level is required.

AUTOMATIC TAPE STOP: An electro-mechanical or electronic device which disconnects the tape drive at the end of a tape or cassette. It may also reset function keys.

AVC (AUTOMATIC VOLUME CONTROL): A circuit used for maintaining constant volume level.

AUXILIARY BASS RADIATOR: An extra speaker cone system used in place of a port in a flapping baffle type of enclosure.

B

BAF (BONDED ACETATE FIBRE): Material used for acoustical damping in some loudspeaker cabinets.

BAFFLE: A structure which keeps the front and rear of a speaker diaphragm separated. This stops the front sound pressure waves cancelling out those from the rear (see also—Infinite baffle loudspeaker).

BALANCE CONTROL: A variable resistor (potentiometer) fitted to stereo amplifiers to manipulate the volume in left or right channel. To help correct stereophonic effect.

BAND: A range of frequencies within two set limits.

BANDSPREAD: The electrical stretching of a section of a wave band to facilitate easy location of the station.

BASS: The low end of the audio frequency range. Below around 150 Hz to 200 Hz.

BASS REFLEX: Type of loudspeaker cabinet with a duct or port permitting enclosed air to be tuned for a coupled resonance effect with the drive unit cone. Results in improved efficiency at low frequencies. Also known as phase invertor.

BASS RESPONSE: The response of an audio frequency system to low frequencies.

BEL: A unit of difference between two volume levels the unit being too large for precise measurements and has therefore been divided into tenths to produce the decibel unit (see dB).

BIAS CORRECTION: Application of small outward pull on the pick-up arm to compensate for natural side-thrust which is an inward pull. See ANTI-SKATE.

C

CANTILEVER: Bar or tube in a pick-up cartridge carrying a stylus at one end.

CARRIER: A high frequency oscillation employed to carry audio signals through space in the form of radio waves.

CARTRIDGE: A small delicate crystal ceramic or magnetic component into which the stylus is fitted. It is situated at the end of the pick-up arm on a record player. Its function is to translate the undulations of the tiny groove on a record into an electrical signal.

CARTRIDGE—8 TRACK: A magnetic recording and play-back system based on a $\frac{1}{4}$ wide endless loop of tape contained in a cartridge. The 8 tracks provide 4 pairs of stereo sound tracks. Tape speed is $3\frac{3}{4}$ I.P.S. and the maximum playing time is approximately 80 minutes.

CASSETTE: A complete two-reel tape unit encased in plastic which can be dropped on to a cassette recorder and played straight away without the need for threading or winding on.

CASSETTE RECORDER: Has a similar function to a reel to reel tape recorder but uses cassette loading type of tape.

CERAMIC: Type of man-made material used in pick-up cartridges.

CHANNEL: The components handling one specific signal for feeding to the different speakers. Separation between channels is an important factor in stereo or four channel reproduction.

CHANNEL SEPARATION: The amount of modulation from one channel which can be heard on the other channel of a stereo or four channel system is usually measured as a dB ratio.

CHROMIUM DIOXIDE TAPE (Cr0$_2$): An improved magnetic recording tape having a Chromium Dioxide coating which, with suitably designed recorders, gives an improved frequency response and a better signal to noise ratio.

COCKTAIL PARTY EFFECT: Name given to our ability to listen selectively to one sound in the presence of unwanted sounds, perhaps of equal intensity. This ability depends on the brain's analysis of the twin signals received by our two ears and is lost on monophonic (single channel) reproduction. Twin channel (stereophonic) reproduction restores part of our ability to separate the various strands of music, for example in orchestral or vocal ensembles.

COLOURATION: Alteration of sound quality by resonance or other peculiarities in an audio system. A particular 'Character' impressed on reproduced sound, often and principally by loudspeakers.

COMPATIBLE: A factor arising from the joining up of a mono and stereo signal in disc reproduction, the term 'Compatible' is used to describe a pick-up arm and cartridge which can be used for either stereo or mono records.

COMPLIANCE: Quality of 'give' or yield associated with a springy or resilient object. Hence the term is used in connection with the pivot within the pick-up stylus assembly.

CONE LOUDSPEAKER: One in which a fibre, paper or metallic cone is mechanically coupled to a magnetic driving unit.

CONE BREAK UP: Effect when a loudspeaker's diaphragm or cone ceases to move as a whole. Usually applies to the higher frequencies and manifests itself by poor transient response and blurred results.

CONTOUR: See LOUDNESS CONTOUR

CONVERSION EFFICIENCY: The ratio of output to input power in a transducer which, with loudspeakers, is the percentage of electrical input available as acoustic output.

CROSSOVER FREQUENCY: The frequency at which a loudspeaker crossover network divides the signal or 'crosses over' from one frequency section to the other.

CROSSOVER NETWORK: A circuit for dividing the audio output of an amplifier into separate frequency bands before feeding the signal to appropriate loudspeaker units. e.g. treble, mid-range and bass within one speaker cabinet. Networks consist of capacitors, inductors and sometimes resistors.

CROSSTALK: Interference between stereo channels. Unwanted signal appearing at the output of one channel expressed as a ratio of the signal in the wanted channel.

CRYSTAL PICK-UP: See PICK-UP (CRYSTAL)

CUEING DEVICE: A system of raising and lowering the pick-up arm at a controlled rate which, by special viscous damping, is independent of the speed at which the operating lever is moved.

CYCLES PER SECOND OR HERTZ: Terms used for sound and electrical measurement. In sound they describe the frequency of vibrations which establishes the pitch of the sounds being measured. The slower the vibration the lower the pitch. A 100c/s (or Hz) note will sound deeper than a 1,000 c/s (or Hz) note. Cycles per second (c/s) was the former name used. The modern term is Hertz (Hz). Their meanings are the same.

D

DAMPING: The process of reducing resonances by the use of resistance or its mechanical or acoustical equivalents.

DAMPING FACTOR: Ratio of loudspeaker impedance to amplifier source impedence. High ratio improves loudspeaker damping, and thus reproduces the signal more faithfully.

DC: Direct current.

DECIBEL (dB): A unit expressing a ratio of two numbers, used when the range can produce excessively large numbers. A tenth of a bel.

DECODER: An electronic device for decoding encoded signals.

DEMODULATION: The process of extracting acoustical information from a radio signal. Also called DETECTION.

DIAPHRAGM: Sound producing elements in a loudspeaker may be a cone driven at its apex or dome driven at its periphery in moving-coil units or a stretched sheet driven over its whole area in electrostatic units.

DIN: DEUTSHER INDUSTRIE NORMENAUSSCHUSS. German Industrial Standards Board; an organisation akin to the British Standards Institute (B.S.I.).

DIN 45 500: A standard agreed by D.I.N. for high fidelity audio products. It covers all elements in the network between cartridge and loudspeaker.

DNL—DYNAMIC NOISE LIMITER: A Philips designed circuit which can be incorporated in the playback amplifier of a tape recorder in order to reduce tape noise principally when it is most noticeable, i.e. during quiet musical passages.

DIODE: A radio valve or semi-conductor device which converts AC to DC.

DIRECTIONAL: Term applied to loudspeakers (microphone or aerial) having greater sensitivity or output in a given direction.

DISCRETE: A quadraphonic sound system which has four independent channels, i.e. 4 channel type. The CD4 disc system is referred to as 'Discrete' since it utilizes two ultrasonic carriers and a matrix to provide the signals for front and rear loudspeaker channels.

DISHED: Term used to describe a faulty record—one that has taken up a slightly dish-like shape.

DISTORTION: When the audio system alters the input sound and adds new frequencies, distortion is occurring. The volume of the added frequencies is expressed as a percentage of the volume of the original, both being measured at the output. Additions or subtractions to or from the input signal are regarded as distortion.

DISTORTION (HARMONIC): The production of harmonics not present in the original signal.

DISTORTION (FREQUENCY): Unequal amplification of a frequency or band of frequencies.

DISTORTION (INTERMODULATION): One frequency interacting with another, to produce a third signal not present in the input.

DOLBY: A noise reduction system for tape. (See pages 94/95.)

DRIFT: The tendency for the speed of a recorder or gram unit to change over a long period, from the correct value. The speed variation is expressed as a percentage of the correct value.

DUAL CONCENTRIC: Type of loudspeaker in which separately driven bass and treble cones are mounted coaxially. In some designs the HF outlet comprises a small horn passing through the LF magnet system and terminating at apex of the bass cone.

E

EARPHONE: A device for converting electrical signals to acoustic vibrations. Fits to the ear and used for personal listening.

EFFICIENCY: See Sensitivity.

EHF: Extremely High Frequency between 30,000 Hz and 300,000 Hz.

EIGENTONE: A type of room resonance produced by parallel reflecting walls.

ELECTRO DYNAMIC: Term commonly refers to moving coil pick-ups and loudspeakers.

ELECTRO MAGNETIC WAVES: The scientific name for radio waves.

ELLIPTICAL STYLUS: Stylus tip with large radius across the record groove and small radius in contact with groove wall. Intended to reduce a form of distortion that arises when playing records. Also called 'bi-radial' tip.

ELS: Electrostatic loudspeaker (also ESL). Transducer employing electrostatic forces to drive radiating diaphragm(s).

EQUALIZATION: A fixed correction applied to a signal to balance known deficiencies in the amplification of certain frequencies.

F

FEEDBACK (Acoustic): Sound building up to a continuous squeal due to the pick-up or microphone picking up a repeat of a signal from a loudspeaker, and feeding it back to the loudspeaker in increasing intensity with each circuit of the sound.

FEEDBACK (Negative): A device for reducing distortion by feeding it back to an earlier point in the circuit in opposition to itself, so that a cancelling effect takes place.

FILTER: A circuit which removes undesirable frequencies from power supplies tuners and amplifiers. In power supplies it removes vitually all traces of AC (to eliminate hum). In amplifiers it prevents amplification of objectionable frequencies, such as record scratch or turntable rumble.

FLAPPING BAFFLE: Type of loudspeaker enclosure based on the reflex principle but employing a compliantly mounted panel, baffle or additional drive unit cone in place of the port.

FLARE (CUT OFF): Frequency at which the acoustic resistance at a horn throat drops to zero. Determined by rate of flare.

FLUTTER: High speed pitch fluctuations produced by uneven turntable, or tape transport mechanism speeds.

FM: Frequency Modulation. A method of transmitting and receiving interference-free radio signals by varying the carrier wave frequency, unlike AM (Amplitude Modulation) which varies the amplitude of the carrier wave. Radio and TV Broadcasts on VHF and UHF are FM transmissions.

FREE-AIR RESONANCE: Natural basic diaphragm or cone resonance of a loudspeaker unit, as measured with the unit mounted on a baffle.

FREQUENCY: The number of times an oscillation or vibration alternates to and fro in one second. One cycle per second, is 1 Hertz (Hz).

FREQUENCY RANGE: Effective operating limits of equipment.

FREQUENCY RESPONSE: The range of frequencies over which audio equipment responds correctly within a variation of a decibel or so. A normal frequency response is 'flat' meaning that all frequencies are equally amplified. The limits of the frequency response occur where the amplification falls below the 'flat' condition. In the DIN specification there is a tolerance within which the degree of amplification at each frequency is allowed to depart from the 'flat' condition.

FUNDAMENTAL RESONANCE: Usually refers to the natural resonance of a loudspeaker cone or cabinet.

G

GAIN: An increase in signal power, usually expressed as the ratio of output power to input power in decibels.

GROOVE: V-shaped track on gramophone record which carries the sound signals in the form of lateral displacements (mono record) or a combination of two 45° displacements (stereo record). Coarse-groove records (about 100 grooves per inch) normally run at 78 rpm. Micro-groove or fine groove records (about 250 grooves per inch) run at 33⅓ or 45 rpm.

H

HALF-SECTION: Type of filter circuit, commonly fitted in loudspeaker crossover networks.

HANDLING CAPACITY: The maximum amount of power or voltage a component (such as a loudspeaker) will handle without overloading.

HARMONICS: The musical overtones which accompany a note. The tuning fork produces a sound with few harmonics, whereas the oboe produces sound rich in harmonics. The audible harmonics produced by playing a piano note are increased if the note is struck more forcibly and for this reason the intensity change is accompanied by a change in tone.

HEADSHELL: Head housing on pick-up arm to accommodate the cartridge.

HERTZ (Hz): The modern unit of frequency measurement, i.e. cycles per second.

HF: High frequency. In the audio range any frequencies above say 2,000 (Hz).

HI-FI: High Fidelity. A very high degree of faithfulness to the original sound reproduced through electronic equipment.

HIGH FILTER: An arrangement of resistors, capacitors or inductors in circuit to introduce a known degree of cut or loss of signal above a certain frequency. To reduce excessive tape hiss or high frequency noise present in a signal.

HORN LOADING: Acoustic load offered to a loudspeaker drive unit by a horn type enclosure.

HUM: A low pitched droning noise usually at frequencies which are harmonics of the mains supply frequency. Hum manifests itself through the loudspeaker when nothing is present in the input signal.

I

IC: Integrated Circuit. A single semi-conductor device designed to perform a number of electronic functions which would normally require a large number of individual transistors.

IMPEDANCE: The ratio of voltage to current in an AC circuit. It is important that input devices (microphone, pick-up, tape deck, etc.) and output devices (loudspeakers or headphones) have the correct 'matched' impedance for the amplifier used. An incorrect impedance match at the input can result in loss of gain, poor signal to noise ratio and a degraded frequency response. A mis-match at the output could also result in damage to the output circuits of the amplifier, though usually only if a loudspeaker having a lower impedance than that recommended is used.

INFINITE BAFFLE (IB): A loudspeaker mounting where there is no air path between front and back of the loudspeaker. Necessitates an air-sealed enclosure.

IN PHASE: The condition which exists when two waves of the same frequency pass through their maximum and minimum values with the same polarity at the same instant.

INPUT: The point at which a signal enters the audio equipment.

IONOPHONE: Type of high frequency loudspeaker unit in which acoustic pressures are generated directly in ionised air by audio modulation of an electric spark discharge.

IPS: Inches per second. Measurement formula for tape speed during record or playback.

J

JACK (JACK PLUG): A connecting device to which wire of a circuit may be attached for insertion into a socket.

K

KC/S: Kilocycles per second.

KHz: Kilo Hertz.

L

LABYRINTH: Type of loudspeaker enclosure with partitions producing a long, convoluted path between rear of drive unit and outlet hole. Lined with damping material to confine resonant effects down to lowest frequencies.

LATERAL RECORDING: System in which the stylus moves from side to side. Stereo disc recording can be considered to combine the two principles through the planes to left and right channel motion. They are effectively at $+45°$ and $—45°$ to the record surface.

LEVEL INDICATOR: Instrument which provides a visual guide to the incoming signal strength, thus permitting adjustments to be made to achieve the optimum level without distortion.

LINE SOURCE: Type of loudspeaker enclosure in which a number of forward-facing drive units are assembled in a vertical line. Offers broad lateral polar response but confined vertical radiation of sound. Mainly used in public address installation.

LOUDNESS CONTOUR: Compensation for the ear's reduced sensitivity to low and high frequencies at low volume levels. It is acheived by boosting extreme lows and highs progressively as the volume level is lowered. In lower-priced equipment this compensation would have to be done manually with the base and treble tone controls.

LOUDSPEAKER: A device for converting electrical energy into sound energy.

LOW NOISE CASSETTE: Cassette using one of the later, improved tapes having a specially prepared iron oxide coating.

LOGIC CIRCUIT: An electronic circuit operating as a 'steering' device to enhance channel separation of a matrix 4 channel system in order to achieve results more comparable to four channel tape.

M

MAGIC EYE: A level indicator embodying a type of cathode ray tube which varies its area of brightness with the variations of signal strength received.

MAGNETIC HEAD: A transducer which converts electrical impulses to magnetic variations for magnetic storage e.g. on magnetic tape.

MAGNETIC TAPE: A magnetic material of a width at least ten times greater than its thickness e.g. a plastic base with a coating of ferric oxide or chromium dioxide as used in magnetic tapes.

MASTER: Original tape or disc recording from which copes are made.

MATRIX: In the electrical sense an arrangement of circuits with intersection between input and outputs to function as an encoder or decoder. When applied to 4 channel sound reproduction four channels are combined into two and then reformed to provide a four channel output.

MC/S: Megacycles per second.

MEGAHERTZ (MHz): One million Hertz= one megacycle/second.

MICROPHONE: An instrument for converting sound waves into electrical impulses. May be mono or stereo.

MID RANGE: Not precisely defined, but is the middle of the audio frequency spectrum between bass and treble.

MODULATION: The process of impressing an audio signal on to a high frequency carrier oscillation. When applied to recording it refers to the change of state occurring. If the change is too severe distortion arises and the recording is said to be over modulated.

MONAURAL: Literally means 'with one ear' but is occasionally used as a misnomer for 'monophonic'.

MOL: Maximum output level.

MONOPHONIC (MONO): Using a single channel of communication, e.g. single channel recording as opposed to stereophonic which uses two channels.

MULTIPLAY: A technique enables successive tape recordings to be made and replayed together on one track.

MUSIC POWER: The amplifier's maximum response at instantaneous peaks of music.

MULTIPLEX (MPX): An extremely complicated system used to transmit and receive stereo broadcasts, i.e. the transmission of two or more channels on a single carrier so that they can be recovered independently at the radio. The multiplex decoder in the radio recovers independently left and right stereo channels from the multiplex signal.

MUTING SWITCH: A switch fitted to audio equipment usually to switch the loudspeakers out of circuit when headphone listening only is required. The switch controlling this is sometimes called a 'muting switch' or silent tuning.

N

NEGATIVE EARTH: Automobile electrical system having the negative terminal of the battery connected to the vehicle chassis.

NOISE: (In acoustics) any extraneous sound tending to interfere with the reception of wanted sounds.

NOISE, AMBIENT: Acoustic noise in a room—environmental sounds. See AMBIENCE.

NOISE, AMPLITUDE-MODULATION: The noise produced by undesired variation of amplitude in a radio frequency signal.

NOISE, BACKGROUND: Of a receiving system. Any audible sound that is not part of the original signal being transmitted.

NOISE LEVEL: Usually refers to the noise signal self-generated in the transistors and resistance of an amplifying circuit expressed in decibels relative to a standard level.

NOISE LIMITER: A circuit designed to limit electrical noise in a system.

O

OBSTACLE EFFECT: Frequency disturbance due to objects in the path of a sound wave reflect only those sounds which have a shorter wavelength than their own dimensions. Longer wavelengths are not reflected but bend round the object. These low frequencies tend to ignore the obstacle while high frequencies are reflected leaving a 'sound shadow' behind the obstacle.

OHM: An electrical unit of resistance and impedance are quoted in ohms.

OMNI-DIRECTIONAL: Having equal output in all directions (loudspeaker), or equal pick-up in all directions (microphone).

ONE NOTE BASS: Excessive low frequency resonance in a loudspeaker, which is responsible for bass notes in the music reproduction tending to have a similar sound or pitch. Very undesirable.

OSCILLATOR: A device for generating an alternating current (AC) electrical circuit. Also a test instrument used for frequency checking. The electrical circuit in a tape recorder which provides the erase and bias currents is an oscillator.

OSCILLOSCOPE: An electronic device which uses a fluorescent screen (like a television set) to display graphs of voltage against time.

OUTPUT: The power, current or voltage delivered by a circuit.

P

PARALLEL TRACK: A technique whereby two recordings on separate tracks can be reproduced at the same time. It is better than superimposing, but can only be done on a 4-track tape recorder.

PEAK POWER OUTPUT: The absolute maximum output power available at any given instant from an amplifier. Equal to twice the RMS power for a sinusaidal signal.

PHASING: Arranging the connections so that the separate signals arrive at and cause the speakers to operate in unison.

PICK-UP (P/U): A device which converts the sound vibrations impressed on a gramophone record into an electrical vibration or signal.

PICK-UP (CERAMIC): A pick-up that operates on the piezo-electric principle but uses a ceramic material such as Barium Titanate. Conditioned to possess piezo-electric properties during manufacture. It is less sensitive than a crystal pick-up to temperature and humidity but has a lower output.

PICK-UP (CRYSTAL): A pick-up the operation of which depends on the properties of a piezo-electric crystal e.g. Rochelle Salt. It has a high output but is sensitive to high temperature and humidity conditions.

PICK-UP (MAGNETIC): The description given to the group of pick-ups which operate on the principle that a current will be produced when a coil of wire is influenced by a changing magnetic field.

PICK-UP CARTRIDGE: The removable part of a pick-up that contains the electro-mechanical elements including the stylus necessary for translating sound from the recorded disc.

PIEZO-ELECTRIC: Property exhibited by some crystalline materials which acquire an electric charge when subjected to mechanical pressure or stress.

PINK NOISE: Section of the audio white noise spectrum used for test purposes on loudspeakers.

PITCH: Quality of sound which determines its position in the musical scale. Subjective equivalent of frequency.

PLAYBACK: Reproduction of a tape recording.

POINT SOURCE: Term applied to a sound source. In sound reproduction usually a loudspeaker in which the effective area from which the sounds are radiated, or appear to be radiated, is very small.

POLAR RESPONSE: Polar diagram, or plotted shape pattern, showing variations of microphone sensitivity or loudspeaker radiation in various directions.

POSITIVE EARTH: Automobile electrical system having the positive terminal of the battery connected to the vehicle chassis.

POWER: (AUDIO): The rate of sound energy produced, expressed in watts.

POWER AMPLIFIER (Audio): An amplifier designed to increase the power of a signal applied to its input, especially where the output is applied to an aerial or loudspeaker.

PRE-AMPLIFIER: A low voltage amplifier which adjusts the signals from microphone or other sources to meet the requirements of its associated amplifier or tape recorder.

PVC: Polyvinyl Chloride. A plastic with many applications, one of which is a recording tape base.

Q-FACTOR: Selectivity of resonance device or circuit. Also used as a symbol in electronics for the quality factor.

QUADRAPHONIC: An audio system capable of working through four channels of sound to give four signals to four separate speakers for full ambient sound reproduction.

QUADRAPHONY: See QUADRAPHONIC

QS SYSTEM: A quadraphonic disc matrix system developed by Sansui Electric, Japan which is similar but not identical to SQ system.

RADIO: The use of electromagnetic waves to transmit or receive electronically generated signals without the use of connecting wires.

RADIO FREQUENCIES: The range of frequencies used for transmitting i.e. from about 10,000 Hz up to many thousands of millions of Hz.

RADIO SIGNAL: The high frequency signal which is radiated by a radio transmitter.

RADIO WAVES: A special form of electrical energy which travels through space at the speed of light. Scientifically known as electromagnetic waves. (see RADIO.)

RATED POWER OUTPUT: The maximum power a given amplifier can produce without exceeding its specified distortion rating.

RATIO: Proportion of value to another often expressed as a fraction i.e. $\frac{1}{2}=$ a ratio of 1 to 2.

RECEIVER: Another term for a tuner.

RECORD CHANGER: A record playing unit that accepts a stack of records and plays them one by one automatically.

RESPONSE: The range of audio frequencies to which a tuner, amplifier, loudspeaker etc., will respond, and the relative amplitude with which these frequencies are reproduced.

REVERBERATION: An effect produced by the gradual decay of sounds reflecting between walls, floor and ceiling. Contributing to ambience.

RF: Radio frequency.

RIBBON LOUDSPEAKER: Means that the coil/cone combination is replaced by a single corrugated ribbon of aluminium, which may be 2 or 3 inches long by about $\frac{1}{4}$ inch wide and acts as coil and diaphragm simultaneously.

RMS POWER: An abbreviation for root mean squared. A power measurement which provides an indication of an amplifiers sustained power capabilities, at a specified distortion level. Bear in mind when looking at power output specifications this simple example—7 watts RMS can be stated as approx. 14 watts peak or 10-12 watts Music Power.

RUMBLE: A low frequency vibration usually of mechanical origin superimposed on the required signal, and associated with record decks.

RUMBLE FILTER: A network of electrical components used to filter out the very low frequencies usually introduced by turntable motors, etc.

RM: Regular Matrix: A means of encoding four audio channels into two and decoding into four used by some Japanese manufacturers.

SELECTIVITY: The ability of a radio to reject stations on channels other than the one being received. The higher the figure (expressed in dB) the better the selectivity.

SEMI-CONDUCTOR: A solid state electronic device is used in place of thermionic valves e.g. diodes and transistors.

SENSITIVITY: The minimum input signal required to produce a specified output signal having a specified signal-to-noise ratio.

SERVICE AREA: The geographical area surrounding a transmitter where good reception can be obtained.

SIGNAL AUDIO: Electrical impulses having a sound origin.

SIGNAL-TO-NOISE RATIO: The difference between the loudest undistorted signal which can be reproduced and the amount of background noise present, expressed as a decibel figure. A signal-to-noise ratio of 50 dB indicates that the maximum signal level is 50 decibels higher than the background noise. From this it will be appreciated that a higher ratio figure means less audible noise.

SILICON (Si): An abundant non-metallic element. It is an intrinsic semi-conductor and is one of the most important materials in the manufacture of transistors.

SINE WAVE: Waveform of a pure tone (a single frequency) encountered when studying the nature of vibrations associated with sounds.

SOLID STATE: A piece of equipment using transistors and using no valves.

SOUND PRESSURE: A measure of sound intensity in terms of deviation from atmospheric pressure.

SOUND WAVES: The variations in air pressure which convey a sound from its source to the listener.

SQUAWKER: Slang term for mid-range loudspeaker unit.

STEREOPHONIC: Multi-channel sound recording and reproduction designed to recreate the dimensional element in hearing, which is absent from monophonic recording. Frequently abbreviated to 'stereo'.

STEREO DECODER: A circuit for receiving a coded stereo broadcast signal and decoding it into two separate left and right hand channels.

STROBOSCOPE DISC: Used for checking the accuracy of the speed of a turntable. When a lamp is lit from an AC mains supply the lines on the stroboscope placed on the rotating turntable may be seen to move to the right or left indicating a degree of inaccuracy. The speed, say $33\frac{1}{3}$ rpm is exact when the lines appear stationary. Stroboscopic discs are prepared for given mains frequencies and are usually marked accordingly i.e. 50 c/s or 60 c/s.

STYLUS: The stylus has replaced the old-fashioned gramophone needle, and bears a diamond or sapphire point. Sapphire and diamond are used because of their hard wearing capabilities.
The Sapphire is a very good compromise for cost against useful life.
The Diamond is acknowledged to be the best substance to use for a stylus.
Both sapphire and diamond styli have a compromise radius at the tip to enable them to play compatible mono/stereo records. However, the highest quality stylus arrangement—and the highest cost—is to have the tip ground in an elliptical way, to give optimum efficiency/quality. An elliptical stylus is nearly always a diamond for stereophonic or quadraphonic use.

SQ: A quadrophonic disc system developed by C.B.S. Laboratories. By means of an SQ encoding matrix four channels can be inscribed on the two track capacity of a gramophone disc which through an SQ decoding matrix can be replayed as four channels.

SUPERIMPOSE: To record on top of an existing recording by cutting out the erase action. This produces a combined recording in which the original will have been damped down very slightly due to the slight erase effect of the second recording.

SYMBOLS:

AC	∿
AERIAL (FM)	⊤⊤
AERIAL (AM)	Ψ
EARTH	⏚
FUSE	⊶
HEADPHONE	◊◊
JACK PLUG	⊏⊐

LOUDSPEAKER

MICROPHONE

PICK-UP P.U.
(STYLUS OPERATED
HEAD)

TAPE

T

TAPE DECK: A recorder which contains no power amplifier or loudspeakers.

TAPE HEAD: Component over which a recording tape is passed. Applies both magnetising field when recording and produces electrical output when replaying.

TONE CONTROL: A device for changing the frequency response of an amplifier. To obtain best audio results for the listener.

TRACK: The continuous pattern of magnetised particles on a tape. Four such tracks can be run parallel to each other within the $\frac{1}{4}$ in. width of standard tape by 'Four Track' recorders.

TRACKING: The accuracy with which the stylus of a gramophone pick-up follows a prescribed path.

TRACKING WEIGHT: Downward force of pick-up stylus tip on the record also called playing weight, or stylus pressure.

TRANSCRIPTION: Term borrowed from professional and studio practice and applied to the more robust and costly turntable. Implies a high standard of performance.

TRANSIENT: Quick fleeting signal involving a sudden change—e.g. from zero to a high strength. Associated with the details of which complex sounds and signals are composed particularly with percussion sounds such as those of cymbals, piano and strings.

TRANSIENT RESPONSE: The ability of an amplifier to respond to the transient of the input signal.

TRANSISTOR: A semi-conductor, fulfilling the same function as a valve which it is rapidly replacing in many types of audio equipment due to its lower current consumption and similar size.

TRANSMISSION LINE LOUDSPEAKER: In this type of loudspeaker, radiation from the back of the drive cone flows down a pipe filled with a low density sound absorbing material.

TREBLE: High end of the sound frequency range, above about 3,000 Hz.

TUNER: Device for picking up radio signals and converting them to high-quality audio signals which can be fed into hi-fi equipment.

TWEETER: Loudspeaker unit intended for use at high frequencies e.g. 5,000 Hz upwards.

U

UHF: Ultra high frequencies. Radio frequencies between 300 and 3,000 MHz.

V

VHF: Very high frequency. Radio frequencies between 30 and 300 MHz. Used for top quality radio transmission. (88–100 MHz.)

VOICE FREQUENCY: The frequency band used for transmission of speech taken to be within 200–3,500 Hz.

VOLT: Magnitude of electrical pressure or potential, number of volts (V.) = **VOLTAGE**

Vu (Meter): Used for the measurement of the level of non-steady signal voltages.

W

WATT: Unit of power. The amount of energy used per second by an unchanging current of one ampere under a voltage of one volt.

WARP: Departure from flatness of a record, resulting in rise and fall of pick-up as it tracks the undulations.

WAVEFORM: A graph showing variations of amplitude against time.

WAVELENGTH: The distance between two successive identical points on an alternating wave.

WHITE NOISE: Random noise covering all audio frequencies without any particular colouration or emphasis. To the ear it sounds like rushing or hissing noise.

WOOFER: Loudspeaker unit designed for use at low frequencies.

WOW: A slow periodic change in pitch due to the non-uniform rate of reproduction of the original sound. Caused by uneven turntable rotation or uneven tape transport past the record playback head.

Index

125